Typical Tributes

'**Deeply revealing** . . . Wareham brings sharp focus to
fathers and sons, masters and whipping boys,
mentors and lovers. The surprise denouement is a delight.'
—Dr. Jess Maghan, psychologist: author, *40 Fathers*.

'**Profound**—universal insights
into childhood, adulthood, loneliness and love.'
—Dr. Brian Sutton Smith
Columbia University professor of psychology

'**Brilliant and compelling...**
reveals the heart and soul
of boyhood... touched me deeply.'
—Brian O'Dea,
author, *HIGH, the confessions
of an international drug smuggler.*

'**Happily destined**, like Milton's *Paradise
Lost* to find it's readers.'
—Vassar University Professor of Literature

'**Inspired**—whimsical, philosophically savvy.'
—Kirkus Reviews

'**Stunning**—an exploration of moral
quandaries ... assured throughout.'
—Publishers Weekly

ALSO BY JOHN WAREHAM

NOVELS
The President's Therapist
Chancey On Top

POETRY
Sonnets for Sinners
How to Survive a Bullet to the Heart

NON-FICTION
Talking Your Way to the Top
How to Break Out of Prison
Secrets of a Corporate Headhunter
The Anatomy of a Great Executive

EXPOSED

How a lost boy bucked the system and found his voice

JOHN WAREHAM

WELCOME RAIN PUBLISHERS LLC

Flatiron Press Edition 2019

First published 2015

Welcome Rain Publishers, LLC, New York

Distributed in New Zealand and Australia
by David Bateman Limited, Auckland

A catalogue record for this book is available from
the National Library of New Zealand.
ISBN 978-1-56649-359-8

10 9 8 7 6 5 4 3 2 1

Text design by IslandBridge
Cover design by John Wareham

Enquiries to The Flatiron Literary Agency of New York:
theflatironagency@gmail.com

Dedicated to
Jack, Von, and Michael

Salutations

Special thanks to my first-form English teacher, Brian Sutton-Smith, who became a lifetime friend. To the masters and comrades at Palmerston North Boys High School who shaped and shared a memorable journey. To Ben O'Connor who taught me, among other things, the value of the throwaway line. To Evan Whitton, Pat Knopf and Ken Bowden, who showed me how to enliven a page of printed words. To my brother Mike, who introduced me to Omar Khayyam. To my late chairman Robert McMurry, who championed my investigations into the science, craft and art of understanding human nature. To Bernard Mindich, Dean Wareham, Tim DeWerff, Dominic Meimen, Craig Rubano, Stewart MacKay and Charles De Fanti, who offered invaluable suggestions. To Welcome Rain chief executive John Weber for his long-term support. To Ian Watt, whose keen eye and publishing sensibility have been an inspiration. To my wife and guardian angel Margaret.

Author caveat

Art is a lie that makes us realize truth, at least
the truth that is given us to understand.

— Pablo Picasso

This is a memoir, not an autobiography. Some say a man can never understand a boy, even when he has been the boy.

Maybe so, but I've given it my best shot. Memory is faulty but truth is important, so I've tried to revisit—then finally make sense of—the inner and outer lives of the boy I used to be, the events that marked his life and stoked his imagination. I've freely confessed what I think he saw and candidly shared what I know he felt.

I've changed a few names, but that's about all. Everything else is more or less as I remember it.

Of all wild beasts,
the boy is the
most difficult to manage.

Plato

Part One
Arrivals

Inside the viewfinder

BY THE TIME we joined the dumbstruck crowd at the corner of Twenty-first Street and Fifth Avenue, only the blazing North Tower was standing. I stepped to the front of the crowd and set Midgie, my little rescue-pup, gently to the pavement. She nuzzled my cuff as I raised my camera and peered through the viewfinder.

With a slow-motion roll and a mounting rumble, the silver citadel began to dissolve. I shot a burst of photos as the crowd behind me gasped, cried out and wept. The castle crumbled, then . . . down . . . down . . . down it tumbled. Now a dense yellow cloud swelled into the yawning, bright-blue, early-autumn sky. I dropped the camera back into the neck-strap and gathered Midgie into my arms. She trembled as we watched and waited, breathing the same dusty, death-filled air. Soon enough, a throng of forlorn, funereal, pasty-faced survivors schlepped up the middle of the avenue. Many were thirty-year-olds clutching briefcases and laptop computers. Most were waiters, workers and secretaries, a rainbow range of nationalities and colours. The stupidity of this wanton assault upon the hardworking innocent was heartbreaking.

Just as depressing was my realisation that I'd missed the opportunity of a lifetime; photo-journalists all over the city would have captured better shots than mine. In the moment the tower began to fall, I should have turned and chronicled the tear-filled faces of my terror-stricken fellow citizens. What an image that would have been.

I aged that day and the clock has been running ever since. Melancholy moods became constant companions. My hair turned silver, and a boyish surgeon transmuted my hip into steel. Then Midgie fell ill. The vet said there was no hope and delivered the fateful injection. She died in my arms and part of me went with her. That night I grabbed a box of my old photos, dropped down on my sofa and ruffled through the images. That's Midgie, see? She's not much bigger than the Coca-Cola can alongside her. And, hey—what about this sepia shot? Is that young fellow me? Really? Whatever happened to *him*? Wherever did he go? If only I could jump into the photo and prep him for the perils—and guilty pleasures—that lie ahead.

Hey, what was that sound?

Was it a chime or a beep?

Maybe it was a knell, for it woke me from my reveries and life has never been the same since. I stepped to my computer, and studied the glowing new email:

Hi John,

Greetings from your old alma mater! We're bringing 40 boys from our commerce class to New York to visit the New York Stock Exchange, meet business leaders, and share life-lessons from long-term Big Apple alumni (a rare breed, as you know). Might you be available to share a few inspiring words with our up-and-comers? It would cheer us all to learn the highlights of your upbringing and school days, and the virtues of the mentors who shaped your dreams.

Kind regards,

Osric White

Department Head / Palmerston North Boys High School

Oh, my! Be careful what you wish for, Mr Alumni-seeker. The less said of my upbringing the better—really. Sure, I chased some dreams and wound up in New York, but nothing quelled the ache of saudade, that longing for something that seems not to exist. As to the virtues of my high school days and mentors, no, no, no! That red-brick corral. That sun-scorched tarmac quadrangle. That ring of shanty classrooms. And who could ever forget the first moments of the first day . . .

—| |—

The fat, intimidating, black-robed first assistant rose like a devil up from hell to commandeer the centre of the steaming, inky courtyard. Glowering through thick lenses encased in heavy charcoal rims, he panned the three-sided battalion of five hundred softly murmuring, grey-uniformed boys standing at ease, army style, hands clasped behind their backs. A bullfrog breath inflated his cheeks.

'ASS-EM-BLY . . .'

Silence fell like a guillotine.

As the obedient throng snapped to ramrod stance, a wispy, bespectacled, third-former got nudged sideways.

'Careful,' he whispered.

His admonition caught the devil's attention.

'You boy! Yes *you!* You boy—*you!* You'll see me after assembly.'

The quadrangle was bounded on three sides by the main red-brick structure, and on the fourth by a rickety collection of retired army huts. The assembly of boys, thirteen-to-seventeen-year-olds, were neatly gathered according to age, intellect and the classroom they were about to enter. Hairy-legged sixth-formers sporting incipient whiskers stood opposite the incoming 'new boys', the third-formers.

The full teaching staff, all male, strode to the front of the assembly and formed a line behind the first assistant. Now the headmaster glided forward. His nickname, Peggy, aptly suggested his ballet-like gait. With his Bible tucked under his arm, he gathered his robe, whisked to the speaker's lectern, set down the tome and gazed over the assembly.

'At the beginning of this new year, let me offer a warm welcome to all of you'—his eyes settled on the third-formers—'and especially to you new boys. We are citizens of a Christian nation, so it is fitting to welcome you with an appropriate reading.'

He cracked the tome.

'Let us contemplate verse sixteen from chapter five in the book of Matthew. "Let your light so shine before men, that they may see your good works, and glorify your Father which is in heaven." Now, to let one's light shine is to do the right thing. It is to possess the courage, the pride, and the self-respect to stand up and be counted. Our beloved school prepares boys to become shining citizens, men who see the difference between right and wrong and who act accordingly. It is by our actions that we are known, and the wise man understands that God is always watching. The shining citizen cultivates no weeds in the garden of his heart. Ignorance of the law of nature excuses no one. Every Christian with a command of reason is supposed to know he ought not to do to another what he would not have done to himself. Any act contrary to that golden rule is to sin. The mere intent to engage in such an act also is a sin. God sees the thought and his judgement follows.'

He snapped the Bible closed, turned on his heel, and disappeared. The other teachers filed out in line behind him. Only the devil remained. He took one step forward, flashed his lenses at your companion, produced his arm and crooked his forefinger.

'You boy—now!'

The waif stepped forward.

The devil produced a long, wicked cane from under his cloak. Seems it was there all the time. He'd been hoping for trouble and had found it.

He grabbed the trembling boy by the scruff of the neck and steered him into the middle of the quadrangle.

'Bend over, boy.'

He held the cane aloft and twitched it.

The new boys winced, but the others knew better.

The devil retreated several paces, stopped and took a deep breath, then broke into a run.

The cane whistled along behind him, then accelerated in an awesome arc and cracked upon the tender rump.

A thousand eyes stared as another five retreats, runs and sickening thwacks rained down.

The devil paused, wiped the sweat from his brow, and contemplated the faint wet red patch that appeared on the offender's thin cotton trousers. Then, puffing through bullfrog cheeks, he drew himself erect and bellowed, 'AS—SEM—BLY, *DIS—MISSED*.'

—| |—

That was the welcome. Could I share such a highlight? And the turning points in my upbringing? But maybe destiny's calling? If so, truth is vital. So yes, I'll deliver 'a few inspiring words'.

But what to say, exactly? Fortunately, this treasure-trove of photos will evoke a few memories. Here, look again. I shot most of them—but not this monochrome of me alongside my mother, Von. That *is* me, right? Well, yes and no. It used to be me. In fact, it is *you*, Johnny— and, now, a lifetime later, years on, I'm talking to you. I mean, you can hear me, right, Johnny? I'll take that as a yes. So, let's see now, you're a five-year-old waif in blue shorts and grey shirt, and you're clutching Von's hand. She was your mother, but she liked you to call her Von. It was quirky, but you loved her for it. Her full name was Yvonne Jean and she looked like the pensive star of a woebegone French movie. She's gazing into the distance from the balcony of that eerie, gothic, rented two-storey hilltop house you called home. I'm right back there with both of you, Johnny. Let me listen in. Maybe, God willing, you and I can have a heart-to-heart talk about what went down . . .

Creators

'LOOK, JOHNNY, Yes, Here they come!' Innocence, apprehension and irony laced her tone. 'All the way back from World War Number Two.' Twenty-five years old, elegant and lost, a radiant fusion of Ingrid Bergman, Greta Garbo and Rita Hayworth.

The scent of spring daffodils infused the morning air. You raised a hand to shade your eyes, Johnny, and then you peered off into the sun-filled, shimmering harbour. Two huge ships, each with three smoking funnels, were delivering Kiwi troops home from their grand adventure.

'They say your uncle Pat got his jaw blown away. We'll hear about that soon enough. See what's left of his tongue, too.'

•

'So you're my little grandson, right?' The matriarch was sharp-featured and sharp-eyed. Her tone and demeanour demanded a reply, but none came. 'If you really are Jack's son, you'll not be lost for words.' Long pause. 'Eh? Come on now—whattayousay?' Nothing fell from your lips. She turned her gaze to your father. 'The kid's got a stutter, Jack!'

'It's nothing,' said Von, softly.

'He'll grow out of it,' said Jack.

'Grow out of a stutter, Jack?' She sounded doubtful. She glanced at Von. 'A stutter, eh?' She turned back to Jack. 'Let's pray that's the poor boy's only problem.' She paused to let that sink in. 'Now it's time for *you* to listen and learn, Jack.' Jack and his mother were both alpha males, or so it seemed. She was the only person who would dare to silence him. Happily, a mantel photo of her as an eighteen-year-old confirmed that she'd been a doe-eyed beauty in her youth. Sadly, she was now slack-jawed, pear-shaped, saggy-breasted and gimlet-eyed. Behind those orbs she was also ambitious, status-conscious, money-hungry and shrewd. 'Pat ran the catering for the troops, fed thousands of soldiers every day, and now he's home to a hero's welcome.'

Jack and his three sisters, his mother and Von had all turned out to welcome the warrior who'd done his bit to save the world. Pat's jaw was somewhat off-centre, but waiting for him to close it was the real problem. He held the floor and rattled on within a parlour room. There was much grandstanding, but little talk of heroic exploits. Perhaps some fellow cook had got fed up with Pat's big mouth and whacked it.

The matriarch smiled at the homecoming conqueror. 'There's money to be made from what he's learned.' She did not stare so fondly at Jack. 'There's no time to lose. Pat's a hero. You boys should cash in right now.'

If Pat was the favourite son, the serpent-tongued mother was the driving force—and, as she well knew, it would take Jack's brains and talent to fulfil her ambitions.

What you did not realise at the time, Johnny, was how any of this—and all this—would play out for you.

Home

'THIS HOUSE gives me the creeps, Johnny.' Von gave a little shudder. 'It has a ghost. It really has. I was here on my own and I heard someone walking around upstairs. I went up and looked.' She shot you a wide-eyed glance. 'Nobody was there!' She shook her head dolefully. 'It was a ghost, it really was.'

Maybe she was right. That musty rented hilltop home could have been the model for the infamous Bates Motel. More likely she was wrong. Maybe the ghost was one of the three boarders who had helped with the rent. One of them was her brother Cecil. He always had a vacant smile. He died at fifty-something, and the cat got let out of the bag. Seems he was a cross-dresser. Maybe he was hiding in a closet.

Boarder number two worked in the Justice department. He was fat and funny, had a great head of grey hair and a way with a bawdy limerick. He had a back corner room with a water glimpse. When he died, you got to look into that room, too. Books! He had a ton of them. You wish you'd never touched them. You touched only two actually. Big medical jurisprudence manuals with pictures, many of them in living colour, of human corpses in all sorts of unhappy states; women with knives through their hearts, kids impaled on iron fences, that kind of thing.

The other boarder, Montgomery, a loathsome pink slug, had the best two rooms in the house—a studio bedroom and an octagonal kitchen/dining room off it with city vistas in all directions. The view was great but he was garbage.

●

'God pays close attention to your prayers.' The Mother Superior's python head floated eerily within the starched white collar that rose like a cloud from her floor-length black habit. 'God doesn't just hear what you say. He also notes what you *don't* say!' A semi-naked young man was nailed to the classroom wall. Sun filled the classroom but the image was chilling. Beneath him and off to the right was a gold and lime reproduction of a woman clutching her child. 'He knows that temptation creeps into human hearts. That's why we say the Lord's Prayer. In the twinkling of an eye, you're in touch with God.' You understood the power of temptation. What struck you most, however, was the notion that a deity could so quickly quell it.

'But nothing is more important than to say three Hail Marys every day.' Her piercing blue eyes searched the room for sinners. 'Now let me tell you, one boy—a good Roman Catholic, just like you, Johnny— befriended a Protestant boy and got led astray. Goaded by the Devil, the bad Protestant boy persuaded the good Catholic boy to steal fruit from the greengrocer and toys from the town. They also told lies to their parents and mocked God. Fortunately, despite his sinning, the Catholic boy made a moment in every day to recite his Hail Marys.'

She poked her head forward and dropped her voice. 'Now, one day, as the two young sinners were walking home from yet another bout of stealing and lying, there came a frightening, angry, orange flash of lightning'—she waved her bony fingers at the ceiling—'and the pavement in front of them yawned open'—she pointed a sharp forefinger to the floor—'and the Devil himself, hissing and spitting fire, lunged out to pull them down into the fiery pits of hell! He instantly snatched up the Protestant boy, who screamed in pain at the red-hot heat of the Devil's piercing claws. Try as he might, however, the Devil simply could not catch the Catholic boy. His three daily Hail Marys had set a protective shield around him. Infuriated at his loss, but happy to at least have claimed one more Protestant life and soul, the Devil dived back down into the fires of hell.' She sighed deeply. 'When you walk home today, I want you to notice the cracks in the footpath that the Devil left behind.'

○

'Oh, Johnny!' Von rolled her eyes and tossed the press clipping back into the photo box. 'Your dad goes on and on about what a big rugby star he was!' She began slowly, then increased the tempo. 'How he, the speedy left-winger, would grab the ball, fend off the defenders, outrun the field, and then, to the roaring cheers of tens of thousands of fans, dive across the line to score the winning points!' She raised her hands and covered her ears. 'B-o-o-o-ring!' She shook her head from side to side, dropped her hands and opened her palms. 'But you know what, Johnny?'—she would say, eyes wide, and sharing a sly grin—'*It's all true.*'

In fact, Jack's dream had been to become a doctor. 'But the depression came and I had to earn a living.' Maybe if he'd joined the medical profession he'd have become less needy for a cheering section. Maybe he'd not have chosen to measure his life by those perishable roars. But if his proudest moments happened on the rugby field, his real-world achievements did not. He built an organisation and masterminded fifteen or so weddings every Saturday. Friday was a big day too. What with debutantes, dances, and balls, he often worked twenty-four hours straight.

It was all leading somewhere, surely.

○

'Just where the hell have you been?' Jack's words woke you. 'All dressed up to the nines like that.' You cracked the door and peered out. The hall was dark, the overhead tungsten light dim.

'To the Friday dance.' She held her perfumed ground. 'You never want to go.' She had a rabbit-fur half-coat over her full-length gown. 'You never want to do anything. You just want to work. I went alone.'

He stepped forward, furious. 'What do you think you're doing? You can't just go out.' He waved his arm in your direction. 'What about him?'

'There are adults in the house. I need some life.'

He grabbed her and shook her. She pulled away. 'You've ripped my dress.' She sobbed and trembled. He clenched his fingers into a fist. She cowered backwards. He stared at her, then turned on his heel and headed out the front door. The floor and walls shook as it slammed behind him.

●

'Oh, Jack!' The sweet object of his affections sucked on her gold-tipped, black Sobranie cigarillo, tossed back her head, and gazed into his eyes. 'Tell everyone about when you scored those winning tries.' His chest swelled and his eyes blazed as he retold the tales. 'Oh, Jack!' She would turn to the hapless listeners. 'He was such a *star*, so *muscular* and *handsome*. He *ran so fast*, and cut such a swathe. He was *Mario Lanza in a rugby shirt*. He truly was!'

Friends evaporated but the Cigarilloed One stayed, as did the rancid scent of the Russian tobacco. A shop girl, he'd met her in his first career as fast-track manager within a retail chain. Before that she'd worked in a mental asylum, as a nurse, she'd say. In fact, she'd merely managed the bedpans. She had a dumpy body and a ferret face, but it painted up okay. As a rugby star and business big-shot he was out of her league. On another level he was easy pickings.

Passages

'WHAT'S HAPPENING?' You dropped your school bag and ran from room to room. The furniture was mostly gone, the beds were stripped bare and the windows were closed. She was standing in the gazebo, gazing at the harbour. The rain had stopped and the clouds were breaking. 'What's happening?'

Her reply was flat and she continued to stare into the distance. 'You know what's happening.'

Well, yes. They were splitting up. You knew that. Something had always been missing, mostly Jack. Like on the night you woke around midnight to the sound of your mother screaming and running out of the house with Montgomery in full pursuit. She, the lithe athletic captain of her basketball team, would surely outpace him. Next morning, the pink slug, expensive leather suitcases and all, was gone from the house. Gone but not forgotten.

●

'Oh, God—the little bugger's fallen head over heels!' The piercing words fell from the wizened lips of the woman known as Winnie. The battered cab had wound its way to a clapboard house in a zigzag street on the side of a hill, close by the wharves, at the wrong end of town. It was a slum dwelling but not entirely without charm. Entry was by way of a steep and slimy staircase directly off the street. No wonder you lost your footing, bumped your butt on each of the dozen or so steps, fell to the bottom and wound up sore, wet and miserable in a murky puddle of rainwater. 'He's all wet. Dirty, too, now!'

The thin lips and beady eyes belonged to the saviour with whom Von would share the burden of the weekly rent. 'Oh, Christ, get up, you little bugger. Come on, this way.' She stepped into the dingy, windowless, nicotine-scented quarters. 'This's the kitchen. It's also the living room—and just about everything else! But we have a fireplace—see? And a bathroom—see, in here.' Yes, indeed. How many bums had rested on that battered, grey iron tank? 'And here's your bedroom. Wazzamatter? The little bugger's turning his nose up! Too good to share with my kids, is that what he thinks? They'll take care of him, no worries. They're older. Smarter, too. You'll see.'

●

'Oh, Jack, you and the car, you're both jaguars!' She tossed her head back and blew the cigarillo fumes into the air. He stood stock still, a yellow dust rag in his hand, basking in the sun, admiring the sheen that bounced from the newly delivered metallic-blue chariot.

'I'm the youngest man in town to buy a Jag.' He nodded in your direction, but spoke softly to himself.

'Oh, Jack, I *bet* you are, I bet that's *true*.' She waved a nicotine-stained forefinger within her fresh bubble of blue smoke. 'You're the youngest *and* you're the smartest. We can both be sure of that, Jack.'

Divorce was a bad word, so Jack stayed on in the haunted house and the Cigarilloed One set herself up in an apartment with a Goldilocks bed. A double bed 'would be too big for the room'. A single bed would 'aggravate my bad back'. So a three-quarter bed was 'just right'. Or as right as right could be back then. Joint custody followed, so you got to spend Tuesday and Wednesday evenings with Jack at the haunted house.

●

On the other home front, Winnie often shared a bed with ex-boyfriends upon their release from prison. They never stayed long, so she welcomed others. If she was loose, the accommodations were tight. Guests shared bunks and seemed happy to do so. That's how you wound up in bed with the fellow who turned out to be Von's dance partner, the dwarflike Chum.

●

The cassocked priest stared coldly at the class. 'The Church says what she means and means what she says.' You'd graduated to the Marist Brothers school, a prison-like, black concrete edifice run by a troupe of zealous expatriate Irish priests aching to share their creeds and catechisms. 'Words matter, which is why we share the liturgy.'

I believe in one Lord Jesus Christ,
the Only Begotten Son of God,
born of the Father before all ages.

Sun from the window hit the bleeding statue.

God from God, Light from Light,
true God from true God,
begotten, not made,
consubstantial with the Father;
For us men and for our salvation
he came down from heaven,

You bowed your head but peeked back up. The priest stared right back at you.

. . . and by the Holy Spirit
was incarnate of the Virgin Mary, and became man.

On it went—

For our sake he was crucified under Pontius Pilate,
he suffered death and was buried,
and rose again on the third day

And on—

He ascended into heaven
and is seated at the right hand of the Father.
He will come again in glory
to judge the living and the dead.

Would it never end?

I believe in one, holy,
catholic and apostolic Church.
I look forward to the resurrection of the dead
and the life of the world to come. Amen.

He's not finished yet, though.

'We say that the Father is God, the Son is God, the Holy Spirit is God, but that the Father is not the Son nor is the Son the Father and the Holy Spirit is neither the Father nor the Son.'

Not a lot of logic in any of this.

'By analogy then we look at the human person, each of whom is a uniqueness—'

Now this bit you can believe.

'But our uniqueness belongs to a nature'—

there had to be a but—

'shared amongst us all, that being our human nature. We are individuals, but social creatures, too, so we need other people.'

The fellow is staring right at you—

'Even individuals who attempt to isolate themselves are dependent on others.'

—|—

Every day, at a quarter of an hour before noon, you all fell to your knees and recited the rosary, finishing to the wail of a lonesome midday siren. You hated catechism. You hated the rosary. You hated having to crouch and pray. But fear of the sadistic, cane-carrying priests trumped everything. There was always homework. Ten parts catechism, one part English, one part maths. To study at that slum-house dining table was hopeless. You gave up and winged it. That worked for a few weeks. Then the priest was on you with his tongue and cane. You dealt with that for a while, but when it became apparent that you'd be shunted into a class for troublemakers under the tuition of a notoriously vicious Brother, you quit the whole goddamn thing.

You rode your bike into town and headed for the pinball parlour. That took cash, so you became a cat burglar. You climbed fire escapes and snuck through unlatched windows into dark, musty hotel rooms. At that time of day the guests were not around, but as your adrenaline raced, you often managed to pick up a stray wallet or purse. Then it was back to the pinball machines. You played this out for several weeks. Finally, alas, the headmaster called Jack and spilled the beans.

●

'What you need is discipline,' he said. You were staying with Jack and he'd arrived home in a fury. The jig was up. He was carrying the electric cord from the iron. He wrapped the lower part of it around his wrist. 'Take off your pants.' You hesitated. 'Take off your pants.' This time you did. You felt naked and vulnerable. 'Kneel.' You hesitated. He grabbed your arm. 'Kneel.' That whip looked lethal. Your body refused to bend. He swung and the cord ripped into your butt. You fell to the floor. 'Discipline.' His face was flushed. The whip continued to rise and fall. Hot urine ran down your legs and formed a yellow puddle on the floor.

Next day your back was black and blue, and wet welts emblazoned your rump. Happily, your trousers and shirt covered everything. Jack drove you to school. Not a word passed. He pulled the Jag to the gate.

He waited and watched until you passed through it, then eased away. You stopped and stepped back. Your bruised legs had minds of their own. They turned and headed into town. It would be a cold day in hell before you surrendered your soul to the Marist Brothers. Next stop was the pinball parlour.

When you limped home Jack was waiting.

'The headmaster phoned.'

He said it deadpan.

You said nothing.

'He said you didn't attend any classes.'

'No.'

'Not any?'

'No.'

'But I saw you walk through the gate.'

'Yes.'

He just stared.

You couldn't tell what he was thinking.

And you didn't much care.

Rosebuds

'WELCOME, THEN, to your new school, Master Wareham.' The youthful counsellor, Brian Sutton-Smith, had a godlike head of golden hair and a warm smile. His office was tiny but neat. A picture window overlooked a garden. 'So you didn't much care for your last school? The religious aspects might have been overdone?'

'It was, uh, depressing, Sir.'

'Ah, depression. It comes and goes. But deep feelings have deep meanings. They bring gifts of awareness and sensitivity. If someone said I could rid myself of depression by giving up those gifts, I would say, *never!* I can endure darkness, but I cannot live without awareness.' He grinned. 'I personally prefer the beach to religion. I take in the sunshine and the sea air. I watch the rise and fall of the tide.' He wandered to the window. 'See those rosebuds? They're perfect. Soon they'll bloom and become all that nature intended. We just have to make sure they get the light and water they need.'

●

'Help, help, I'm being beaten and raped!' There was a bit of a problem with the woman next door. On the plus side, you were living with Von whose two-bedroom clapboard cottage was only a couple of blocks from your new school. Both the house and the suburb were run down. Whenever anyone passed, the crazy neighbour would stick her head out of her second-floor window and shriek. She lived alone, so nobody took much notice, though Chum sometimes laughed and shouted back.

●

'Might be dangerous for a boy of your age to read that.' School was out and no one would be home until after six o'clock. After wandering around town, you found the battered book in a bin in a second-hand store. The fuzzy concentric circle on the cover was intriguing. *Hypnotism: How to Tap the Full Power of Your Personal Magnetism.* Might be just the advice you need. There was no need to steal it. The proprietor scanned the pages. 'But maybe not. Okay kid, it's a gift. Just don't come back in here, right?' You walked back home, propped yourself on sagging wire of your narrow bed, and skipped straight to the important page:

> Hypnotizing yourself is easy. Find a quiet and peaceful place. Turn off all radios and phones so your trance won't be disturbed. Stand straight with your feet on the floor. Pick an object at eye level and stare at it. Take some deep breaths. Imagine tension escaping your body. Feel your eyelids grow heavy and your mind switch off. Continue deep breathing. Feel your facial muscles relax. Once you have achieved your goal, power up your energy and awaken. You will now be free of the delusions that have been leading you into the wrong things.

●

'V-O-C-A-B-U-L-A-R-Y.' The golden-haired counsellor wrote the word in neat capital letters with purple chalk. 'Our *vocabulary* is the stock of words we use to explain our thoughts and feelings.' He was jacketless, but neatly turned out in grey trousers, yellow shirt and plain blue tie. He spoke with infectious enthusiasm. 'The bigger the better! That's why we start each day by adding to your stock of words, and making sure you can spell them!' No catechism and no prayers. It was like escaping a medieval dungeon and entering a sunny garden.

●

'What've you got there, Johnny?' Von peered over your shoulder as you tore open the plain brown wrapper. Advertisements at the back of magazines had always intrigued you. 'Oh, goodness me, Commando Judo! My sweet little son sent off for a book on Commando Judo.' She was more amused than surprised. 'Where'd you get the money?'

'Saved it.'

'Bet you didn't.' She grinned, then shot off out the door in her rabbit coat. You consoled yourself with the scent of her perfume.

●

Jack wasn't in the room at the time. Just you and the Cigarilloed One. 'Here's something you should see,' she said. She set a framed photo onto the mantelpiece. 'We had a little ceremony and got married. Just a quiet little Presbyterian service with a few adult friends. I wore my tailored suit.' You peered into the photo, a head-and-shoulders monochrome shot garnished with smudgy photo oils. 'Coloured it myself,' she said. He looked guileless. She did not. The tinctured smile was as tight as the bulging buttons on her flannel jacket. She'd put on weight. She looked like a pig in a safari suit.

●

Commando Judo called for close attention. Yes, you'd bought the little tome with money you stole from Jack's trousers. But that was okay. You were the smallest kid in the class so the manual was an investment. The contents were as described. It was an authentic American short course, in words and pictures, showing how to disarm and defeat an enemy in hand-to-hand combat. To defend against a knife attack, one had to learn how to block the enemy's descending blow, grab the arm with the knife, slip your leg behind the fellow, toss him backwards onto the ground—then 'jump onto the exposed groin, HEELS FIRST!' Fantastic. If an enemy attempted to kick you, step back, grab the offending heel at the apex of the swing and thrust upwards. The enemy would fall rudely backwards to the ground, damaging his skull and exposing his vulnerable genitalia. You managed to persuade a friend to practise the opening moves. The ability to effect a wrist throw came naturally and quickly. Such skills were comforting.

Paybacks

'PERHAPS YOU ARE TRYING to steal this fruit because you were a monkey in an earlier life?' The turbaned shopkeeper smiled as he removed the banana from your hand. 'Don't be afraid to speak up.'

'I, uh . . . uh . . . I, uh . . .'

'Oh, a stutter—poor boy.' He set an amber hand upon your shoulder. 'Karma! A cosmic plan is unfolding. You are part of a never-ending rising and falling. You must ride the wave or drown.'

His eyes were warm, his hand as soothing as his voice. The smell of the vegetables, the feel of the sawdust floor beneath your feet, the drift of the scales hanging from the ceiling, even the walls themselves – everything seemed to disappear.

'If karma caused my stutter, can karma cure it, too?'

'Seems it just did!'

'It comes back, always.'

'Of course! Karmic law is simple. Every experience is repeated until you apprehend it properly and fully the first time.'

'The first time?'

'Karma runs backwards. There is no reprieve for past misconduct. You dodged it then, so you must suffer now. Your money is no good here. One cannot undo what has happened. Happily, the inexorable march of time offers opportunities for redemption. So do not try to escape. Stay in this world and do your karma. You are worth fighting for. To serve karma, we must repay good karma to others.'

'Do unto others?'

'Oh, religion!' He shrugged and wiped his hand on his blue and white apron. 'Religion only gets us so far, karma takes care of the rest.'

'You were never a Christian?'

'I sometimes wish I had been. Blind faith that God is doing the right thing might be wonderful. I console myself that we Buddhists have more control over what life delivers, and that we can change our karma.'

'My stutter can be fixed?'

'You can't control results, only actions. We are heirs to our actions. They're like ships we set out to sea but don't know when or with what cargo they'll be returning. Small things matter, too. Tiny drops of water fill huge vessels, and a single spark can burn down a haystack. If you sit and watch, karma can be pure entertainment. So relax. Today you're alive and blessed with good fortune.'

'It's good to stutter?'

'Karma, like gravity, is so basic we seldom notice it. It is because you stutter that I am making a gift of this banana. It is because you stutter that I am sharing my wisdom. Look down this street. People are going about their business. A tram is coming and, as it approaches, the descending sun is sparkling in the rails. You see it, yes? It is beautiful, no? Today exists, tomorrow does not. I am an old man today, yet a young man forever. There is only now. Please look. This beautiful sunset will never happen again, never. Do not fret about karma, yours or mine.'

●

'Got 'em mangled in an accident,' said Chum. He grinned and flexed his so-called fingers. The middle index finger of his right hand was totally missing, and the claw-like pinkie on the left hand had been reaffixed. The others were either stumps or missing. They looked grotesque but functioned perfectly. He had a shock of ginger hair and a pleasant smile and was a regular visitor. He and Von had a weird circle of friends. Winnie dragged along a current beau. On Saturday nights they'd smoke and drink and get up a card game. Well, Von never smoked and rarely drank, but the others made up for that. On Sundays the place reeked of stale smoke and beer. Chum was a chain smoker and a winner at cards. His dexterity with a deck was incredible. You were five years old when first he fondled you. There was a thrill to the touching, right? A magic to the masculine whiff of his nicotine breath. A majesty to the power of his male member that was almost mesmerising.

> *Have the subject place his right palm on top of your left, while you both sit face to face. Now say, 'Look at my eyes and continue looking until I say something. In a moment I will count to three. Press down on my hand and I'll be pressing up against your energy.' Now begin counting, then say, 'Push, Push, Push.' Now put your right hand over the subject's eyes in a shading and caressing action and say, 'As you press down on my hand I want you to develop a feeling in your eyes like you're up much too late at night watching an old movie, you should go to bed but you're just so tired. You feel your eyes so droopy . . . and closing . . . and drowsy . . . and . . . SLEEP!' The moment you say 'sleep' slip your hand away from the subject. Practise on your friends and family members and you will see results.*

●

'Here you are then, you little devil.' She smiled as you studied the yellow carton. Chum was standing beside her, grinning. 'Go on then, open it.'

'Thanks, Von.' You held the box with one hand, and wrapped your spare arm around her. She was soft and perfumed. It was kind of awkward. She was never into shows of affection.

'Don't just look—open it. It's a Kodak Brownie, see. Just like mine, but better. It's the one you had your eye on in that shop window.' You extracted the camera from the carton. 'And here's a roll of film to go with it.'

'It has eight shots,' said Chum.

'We'll pay for one roll a week. Developing and printing, too. The guy in the shop says it'll keep you out of mischief.' She laughed. 'Not for long is what I said.'

'Yeah, not for long,' said Chum.

○

Mickey Spillane! What a writer! He sure knew how to make the real world go away. And what a finish!

> *The roar of the .45 shook the room. Charlotte staggered back a step. Her eyes were a symphony of incredulity, an unbelieving witness to truth. Slowly, she looked down at the ugly swelling in her naked belly where the bullet went in. 'How could you?' she gasped.*
>
> *I had only a moment before talking to a corpse, but I got it in. 'It was easy,' I said.*

Wow! Who'd have guessed she was the villain all along? You closed the book and studied the cover. *I, the Jury.* So, the jury was the guy with the gun pointed at the midsection of that sexy blonde undoing the bottom button on her open blouse. Her full orange lips matched the colour of her skirt, loose and ready to fall. Yes, indeed—*Passion, Crime and Suspense*—as promised.

○

'They'll make a man of him, Jack.' The Cigarilloed One exhaled. 'Boarding school will bring him into line.'

Bring him into line?

'They'll mould him into a gentleman.'

Mould him?

'They'll turn him into a real man, Jack. It was your school, and my goodness'—she pursed her lips and pushed her face up into his—'what a man they made you! In his case it won't be easy, though'—she turned, cold-eyed, back to you—and he'll be in for some big changes, won't he, Jack?' She folded her arms. 'Big changes.'

'I've had a word to Gus. He'll look out for you, Johnny. We used to be classmates, both represented the school at rugby and at cricket. Now he coaches the first fifteen. Served as an infantry officer. Saw his men killed and faced a firing squad himself. Wrote a book about it. Got himself published all over the world. He'll be headmaster soon enough.' He paused and smiled. 'I have a going-away present for you.'

'You're gonna give him a present?' She was miffed.

'A camera. He likes photography.'

'He already has a camera.'

'This one's special.'

'Oh, Christ, you got him a Leica!'

You opened the scuffed, brown-leather carry-case. The camera was old, and the black outer enamel was tired. You didn't care. It was a Leica and the lens was good.

'Thanks, Dad, I love it.'

Part Two

Salad Day Encounters

Greetings

'THAT'S THE MAIN BUILDING, JOHNNY.'
Jack slowed the Jag to a crawl and gazed wistfully at the utilitarian, turn-of-the-century, one-storey red-brick building. 'I was always in the A-stream.' The chariot glided on. 'And there's the sports field.'

'You starred in rugby *and* cricket, Jack.' She stubbed her cigarillo in the ashtray, then straightened her new hat.

'You'll love it here, Johnny, it'll be fun, you'll see.'

The Jag pulled in to rest alongside the gate of a commodious two-storey, yellow stucco building.

A tall, thin, bespectacled man in greys and a tweed jacket appeared. 'Aha, a gleaming carriage has arrived,' he said, stepping to the driver's window. 'I'm Stowe, the housemaster—and if I'm any judge, you're Jack Wareham, the illustrious Old Boy. Welcome!' He peered in through the window. 'So you must be Johnny, the precious cargo.'

Jack stepped onto the warm asphalt road, and offered his hand. 'I'm sure all the boys who arrive at these gates are precious cargo.'

'Indeed.'

They extracted your bag from the car boot.

'We're just gonna drop him and go, right, Jack?'

He turned to you and smiled wanly. 'It's the beginning of a new life, Johnny, so I think you'll be happiest if we just drift away.'

'Will he have a bicycle?' asked Stowe. 'Most everything is walkable, but the boys have bikes to to-and-fro to the town and to some of the gladiatorial events.'

'You should know, Jack, you were one of the greatest gladiators.' She caught Stowe's eye. 'He played for the first fifteen *and* the first eleven, you know.'

'My wife has the matter of the bicycle in hand.'

'I'm getting him something special, Jack. It'll arrive on the train, next week. He can pick it up from the station.'

'Meantime, you'll have your Leica to keep you company, Johnny.'

●

The whipping boy winced but shot you a half smile. He seemed a kindred spirit. A soft word might ease his pain. 'Are you, uh, are you . . . uh, are you okay?'

'I'm bleeding, actually.' He was holding back tears. He tapped the frame of his tortoiseshell glasses. 'They call me Shell. I kind of like it.'

'I'm Johnny. I saw. We all, uh, saw. It was, uh, terrible.'

'It truly was.'

'I can make the pain go away.'

'Really?'

'Put your palm on mine.'

'You're kidding, right.'

'Look into my eyes. Keep looking. You're ready, right? One . . . Two . . . Three . . . Push down. You're up late at night . . . you should go to bed but you're just so tired. You feel your eyes so droopy . . . and closing . . . and drowsy . . . .'

'It's working.'

'Really?'

'Donum potest esse distractio.'

'Huh?'

'It's Latin—'distraction can be a gift.'

'I guess.'

'You're a boarder, right? Me too.'

The student body comprised five hundred boys. Most lived within the community and were 'day boys'. Some bicycled home for lunch, but most brought cut lunches prepared by doting mothers. Fifty-six boys, mostly from farming families, boarded at College House. Fourteen of the boarders were 'new boys'. Fourteen were in their second year, fourteen in their third, eight in their fourth and six in their fifth. Kiwi kids could join the workforce at age fifteen, so numerical slippage was normal, and most boarders quit early to work on the modest family estates.

●

'So, you're Jack's son.' Gus Wilson pulled you aside on the way into the first class. He was a handsome man's man with ginger hair and a pockmarked face.

'Uh, yes, uh, Sir.'

'Hmmm, I see. And you're settling in?'

'Yes, Sir.'

'Well, you made the A-stream, so you'll be in my Latin class.'

'Yes, Sir.'

He strode off.

Settling in?

●

The moment the devil appeared in the doorway you forgot about the invasive scent of the freshly varnished classroom walls. Out of the darkness he came, swirling across the floor, clutching at his black robes, holding tight to the cane tucked under his left elbow. He tossed two books onto the corner desk facing the room.

'Third-formers do not typically inspire respect.' The soulless eyes, magnified by the thick lenses of the black-rimmed spectacles, surveyed the thirty students jammed into a newly renovated classroom. 'But I'm told this particular class comprises the best and the brightest.' A hardcover copy of *The Golden Treasury of English Literature* sat on each desk. Your classmates mostly knew each other. You were the outsider, the new boy. Shell was directly in front of you, trying not to shiver. To your left, a large set of windows overlooked a couple of fine old oaks. 'So I shall hold every last one of you'—that devil was talking directly to you, Johnny—'to the highest possible standard.'

The devil was wrong about the future but right about the present. Students had indeed been sorted according to their imagined intellectual gifts. Those judged capable of becoming doctors and lawyers were in the 'Professional' stream. They would learn Latin, mathematics, science and literature. Those not so gifted were 'Commercial'. They would be schooled in basic reading and arithmetic, and the ins and outs of business. Many boys hailed from local farms so there was also an 'Agricultural' stream. They would focus their talents upon earthy things, and the ins and outs of animal husbandry.

'I shall lead you, shall lead every last one of you, come what may, to the deepest literary understanding that diligent boys can imagine.'

Yes, it was indeed the selfsame satan who'd wielded the courtyard whip. His nickname, Soapy, stemmed from the devilishly moist complexion.

'Let us turn to the genius of William Wordsworth and his everlasting classic, "Daffodils". You, boy,'—adding insult to injury, it pointed to Shell, the object of its earlier affections—'read the poem.'

I wandered lonely as a cloud

'Don't simper, boy. Read it aloud. *Aloud.*'

That floats on high o'er vales and hills

'No, no! That's not *reading.*' The devil waved a cloven hoof. 'Who can read aloud? Read without whimpering? Do I see a hand? Yes, you boy, you in the back there.'

When all at once, I saw a crowd
A host of golden daffodils.

'That's better. Much better.'

Beside the lake, beneath the trees,
Fluttering and dancing in the breeze.

'Now listen closely. The poet is saying that while wandering like a cloud floating above English hills and valleys, he encountered a field of daffodils beside a lake.'

Such insight.

'The four six-line stanzas of this poem follow a quatrain-couplet rhyme scheme, ABABCC, and each is metered in iambic tetrameter.'

Such wisdom.

'The dancing, fluttering flowers stretched endlessly along the shore, and though the waves of the lake danced beside the flowers, the daffodils outdid the water in glee. The poet could not help but be happy in such a joyful company of flowers. Ah, what wealth the scene would bring him! Let us skip to the last verse.' Now the devil himself reads:

For oft, when on my couch I lie

Often lying on a couch would be the norm for this fat devil.

In vacant or in pensive mood

Devils can be pensive?

They flash upon that inward eye

That evil eye.

Which is the bliss of solitude

To escape from this hellish room would be blissful.

And then my heart with pleasure fills

Your heart?

And dances with the daffodils.

'The characterisation of the sudden occurrence of a memory—daffodils that "flash upon the inward eye"—is psychologically acute, but the poem's main brilliance lies in the reverse personification of its early stanzas.'

As you say, Sir.

'The poet is metaphorically compared to a natural object, a cloud, and the daffodils are personified as human beings, dancing and tossing their heads.'

Golly! Who'd have guessed?

'This technique implies an inherent unity between man and nature, making it one of Wordsworth's most effective methods for instilling in the reader the feelings the poet so often describes himself as experiencing.'

So, there it was. In mere minutes the devil created a hell on earth and picked a lovely poem to death. From that moment on you withdrew, comatose, into that safe, silent centre of the brain.

When you woke the devil was gone.

'What's next?'

'Mathematics.'

'Who will teach it?

'Grubby.'

'Grubby? Why do they call him grubby?'

'You'll see.'

Gripping a bamboo switch, he bustled through the door clad in a stained brown Harris tweed sports jacket. A blemished orange tie sagged within a frayed blue shirt, in turn unhappily tucked into baggy, grey, pee-stained trousers. He paused to savour the silence, then, eyes bulging, raised the cane above his head. 'Any boy who does not pay attention,' he thundered, spraying spittle upon the front row, 'will be disciplined thusly!' He crashed the cane upon the desk, narrowly failing to remove a set of thirteen-year-old fingers.

Thusly—the coinage was peculiar but the intent clear.

So, there was no mistaking Grubby. He stepped to the blackboard, drew a box, then took a half-step back and pointed the cane to his handiwork. 'In Euclidean geometry, a parallelogram is a simple, non-self-intersecting quadrilateral with two pairs of parallel sides.'

The cane was slim and green. Was it slightly thicker at one end than the other? Yes. It tapered from the thick end wrapped in his dirty fingernails, to the business end now whistling wanly as he waved it over the class.

'The opposite or facing sides of a parallelogram are of equal length and the opposite angles of a parallelogram are of equal measure.'

His eyes were bloodshot. His teeth were yellow. An incisor was missing from the lineup. Clumps of stubble infested his raw complexion. His breath was stale and blobs of foam clung to the corners of his mouth. On the merciful side, even as he puffed and bellowed, his voice seemed to be fading.

'The congruence of opposite sides and opposite angles is a direct consequence of the Euclidean Parallel Postulate and neither condition can be proven without appealing to the Euclidean Parallel Postulate or one of its equivalent formulations.'

The mouth was moving but the volume had all but vanished.

'The three-dimensional counterpart of a parallelogram is a parallelepiped.'

Those pasty spittle blobs were growing by the moment.

Perhaps this was all a dream. No such luck.

—⊢⊢—

Morning break, what a relief. You sat on one of the benches surrounding the quadrangle, and soaked up the sun. So, this was boarding school. Soapy and Grubby were doubtless the worst of the teaching bunch. Happily, a fatherly friend was to immerse you in the mysteries of Latin. Hoping to learn a little more about this tutor, you meandered inside to check out the team photos that adorned the dark, musty main corridor.

Sure enough, the black-framed fading photos of 1930s first rugby fifteens and first cricket elevens contained images of J. Wareham and G. E. Wilson. Arms crossed, fit and strapping, their daunting poses suggested ambition and inner self-belief. They knew they had earned the right to be on the team, and to have their images preserved on this wall of heroes to inspire incoming generations. You wandered back to the classroom and reclaimed your chair within the murmuring flock.

Then, through the open door, you all caught sight of Wilson and silence descended. But he did not enter. Instead, he waited in the corridor, twitching a cane. A frail, fourteen-year-old fourth-former appeared.

'Bend over, boy.' Wilson waited a moment, expressionless, then, with the entire class peeping through the open classroom door—which was doubtless the reason for selecting this particular location—he delivered the preparative lesson. One . . . two . . . three . . . four . . . . Ah, yes—the swish of the cane and the thwack as it landed whistled through the corridors. The intensity of the strokes was as brutal as it was bewildering. The good-hearted fatherly guide, the anticipated guardian angel, might just be a critter to be feared.

Wilson dismissed the whipping boy, then calmly entered the room and slid the cane out of sight behind the desk.

'Raise your hands, those among you who have already studied Latin in your final year of intermediate school?' Shell raised his hand, as did several others. 'Well, you'll have an advantage as we compress what you already know into the next thirteen weeks. For now, I'd like you all to open your textbook to the page that shows the declensions of the noun "table".' Sun streaming in the window created shadows in his deadpan, pockmarked face. 'Now, a noun in Latin is the same as a noun in English. It is a person, place, thing or idea—or, as before me here right now, a table.'

> *Person, place, thing, idea. . . . Wilson was the person, this was the place, Johnny was the thing—and the big idea was that the omniscient threat of violence would lead to ultimate enlightenment. He seemed genial enough now, but the coldness with which he delivered those four strokes was also on display. Perhaps he was even darker than the others.*

'If something is a noun in English, then it is also a noun in Latin. But a noun in Latin also tells a lot about the noun. For example, let's think about this form of the Latin noun for table, "mensam". When you see "mensam" you know that it is almost certainly feminine, is probably the direct object of a sentence and is singular.'

Oh, God. He's going so fast. How can anyone follow this? Feminine . . . direct object . . . singular. . . . Might you be too effete for this fellow's taste . . . and become the singular object of his wrath?

'To compare that to English, let us look at the English word 'table.' We can see that it is singular, because the plural is "tables".'

Whatever is he talking about? Tables. . . . Only once did you share a dining table with Jack and Von. You'd raced home from school, five years old, reeking of urine. They were whispering, but stopped as you entered.

'What else can we learn about the word? It isn't necessarily a direct object; it could be a subject—the table is large; or an indirect object—I walked to the table; or it could be a direct object—He kicked the table.'

It's gibberish and you're lost. Who cares? Not you . . . You walked to the table and Von smiled. Nobody kicked the table. She merely dashed from the room and returned carrying a fresh change of clothing.

'Also, we don't know its gender because English doesn't use a gender system for nouns.'

So now he's on a gender bender. . . . Gender . . . You washed way the urine, donned your fresh clothes, and returned to the dining table. Von set a bowl of soup down for you. Soon after that, they split. There was only one gender in this room. Where might Von be now?

'So, why are we able to see these things about Latin words? We know them because Latin nouns "decline"—they change their endings to fit their usage.'

What is declining here, is your interest in learning Latin. Maybe the way to change a fellow's ending is to welt his bum. Enlightenment will result in fitter usage.

'What really throws a wrench into this is that in addition to masculine and feminine, Latin also has the neuter gender. "Crustulum", a biscuit, is a good example of a neuter noun.'

A wrench and a neuter,
the stench of a tutor

'Now, Master Wareham,'—the eyes focused sharply—'why is a biscuit neuter but a table feminine?'

Why indeed? One is edible and one is not? No? Then perhaps a biscuit might comfort a boy who had been neutered? Maybe the table could serve as a whipping post for effete young fellows?

'Cat got your tongue, Wareham?'

'St . . . st . . .—'

'Stutter? Ah, yes. Yes, of course. A *stutter*. We can deal with that.' The eyes sharpened. 'When you complete your homework, hand it to me. I'll read it aloud for you.'

Oh, no—a compromise to bridge your retardation! But if this cold-eyed faux uncle's gonna inspect your homework, everything you deliver has to be perfect.

'Well, Master Wareham, the simple answer to my question is that sometimes the gender of Latin nouns makes no sense at all.'

Just like you, and life itself within these arid walls.

'In our next class we'll learn about the first declension and the nominative and accusative cases. For now, you have a working knowledge of what constitutes a Latin noun. You know that each noun belongs to one of the five declensions and one of the three genders.'

What I know is nothing.

'You know that the six cases are nominative, genitive, dative, accusative, ablative, and vocative.'

Absolutely nothing.

He retrieved the snake and shared a glance. 'Your homework is prescribed at the end of chapter three in your textbook.'

Soldiers

'PLAT—OON—ATTEN—SHUN!' This was different. A confident, thick-set third-form schoolboy dressed up as a soldier-doll. He held his decorated chest high, mindful of his mission. The idea, apparently, was to create a fighting force ready to defend attack upon the homeland. You snapped to attention. He passed slowly down the line, carefully inspecting his subordinates. An admiring Wilson, neatly decked out, presumably in his former army uniform, stepped along behind him. Most boys were wearing their uniforms, abrasive khaki shorts and jackets. Yours would come later. For now you only had a soldier cap with no brass buttons.

The military manoeuvres over, you sat on the grass, sipped the sunshine and vacantly gazed at College House in the distance.

'I'm Ted.' You looked up into a keen pair of blue eyes. 'I'm new to everything.'

'Boarder or day boy?'

'Boarder. Lot of fun and games, today—eh?'

'Dunno. Where's the, uh, enemy?'

'It's not about war. It's about discipline and mental toughness. Helps with everything. Especially rugby.'

A shadow fell across your bare knees.

'Listen, chaps!' You glanced up. It was the soldier-doll. 'You're wondering what it's all about?' He was poised beyond his years. 'Well, it's about spirituality, not physicality. It's about becoming *citizens*— and doing what's right for the country.' He smiled, nodded and strode off.

'That was Upton Wright. Head boy at his last school, I'm told. You can see why he got promoted straight to platoon leader.' Ted gave a mock salute then mimicked the soldierly voice, 'Carry on, chaps.' He nodded then glanced back to you. 'He's prefect material, of course.'

As in class-ridden Mother England, whence the custom came, the best and brightest of the upper-sixth-form boys were appointed prefects. They were to be models for the lower forms. They enjoyed special privileges and conducted themselves in the manner of English gentlemen. They served themselves first at all meals, had their own private meeting room and dispensed discipline, including canings. Being colonials, however, their lowly birth would ultimately deny them the authentic royal status. Meantime, for most of these fellows, the notion of showing themselves to be a cut above the common herd was not without appeal. Not so subtle changes appeared in their accents, demeanours and behaviours. They became more confident, expansive and dismissive, a law unto themselves. It was intriguing— and depressing—to watch credulous outlanders morph into prigs.

•

Hsssssssss. As you stood on the station platform a cloud of coal-fuelled steam hit your eyes, nose and ears. You ran down the dusty platform to the uniformed attendant. He poked his cap back on his head. 'Looking for something, Boyo?'

'A bike. I'm, uh—'

He pulled a paper from his pocket. 'You're John Wareham, right? Your velocipede awaits'—he pointed his forefinger—'down there in the cargo carriage.'

The public transportation system in this lonely town was hopeless, but the place was dead flat so just about everybody owned a bike. Most boarders had three-speed bikes, but new boys often arrived with the latest ten-speed racers. Colours varied, many were black, some were red, a few were blue. They bore fancy golden lettering and emblems proclaiming their British origins. A ten-speed Raleigh was cock of the walk.

Only one bike waited in the open carriage. Its ancient black frame was battered. There was no front light and no stand. The wheels were ugly, the spokes were rusty and the tread was all but gone from the incongruous balloon tyres. Only the hard leather seat gleamed, doubtless from the application of several generations of assholes. It was a truly ugly thing. A knot of brown twine attached a thick yellow card to the frame. It bore your name in the black ink script of the Cigarilloed One.

You tore the card from the twine, then jumped back into the platform shadows. You'd tell them it never arrived. She'd profess the loss a mystery. Jack would quietly find out what kind of bike the other fellows had and get you one of those.

Here's that hiss again. The platform shook beneath your shoes and the coal steam rose into the grey sky. As the train disappeared you felt sadness for the Auckland-bound contraption. No one would know its story. No one would know what to do with it.

●

What to do? That Latin exercise at the end of chapter three looked daunting. Turning in a paper to satisfy Wilson might be impossible. Mediocrity would not do the trick and perfection was out of the question. You sat on the prep room bench and thumbed backwards through the book. What to do?

'Need some help, Johnny?' It was Shell. 'I've done it already, see.' He pointed to an open page in his exercise book. Not a blot, blemish or correction.

'Oh, uh, I dunno, Shell. I mean is that, uh, okay?'

'Of course. Everything's okay. I was first in Latin last year.'

'But if I copy I won't learn. Anyway, someone will, uh, find out.'

'I won't tell anyone. Wilson will never know. We're friends, right?' Such perfect pages, might they be a gift from the gods? 'Use mine this time, Johnny, and I'll help you catch up later.'

Shell was lonely as well as brainy. He needed friendship and admiration. To fill that void or turn away? Might you fall into the triangle of dishonesty? What were those three sides again? Need, Opportunity and Excuse? Need—yes! You needed to turn a perfect piece of homework to satisfy Wilson—Gus, as they called him behind his back. Opportunity—yes! Shell was offering—desperately wanted, in fact—to sate that very need. But Excuse? Wait! Yes, wait. Forget all about that silly triangle. You'd be giving help and getting help. You'd be forging a sacred bargain. Yes! By copying Shell's homework you'd salve a fellow sufferer's loneliness. That would be a virtuous act, surely. And a virtuous act needs no excuse.

●

Respectful silence reigned. Wilson, master of the hot-and-cold cane and the three genders, was expected to enter. But no such bad luck. Instead, clad in a moist tracksuit, Ian Colquhoun, the master known as Coke, loped through the door. Though more than six feet tall, he perched himself on the front desk, tucked his legs beneath him, folded his arms around his knees, and pulled his fists to his chest. Only a receding chin and a shaft of oily hair sticking out sideways sabotaged the Mr Cool presentation.

'I'm standing in for this class,' he said. The nasal Kiwi accent had been buffed. Even in New Zealand, a gym teacher was a low man on the teaching totem pole. The nickname, Coke, aptly conjured the image of a brittle brain. He blinked. Or was that a twitch? 'Now which one of you is Master Wareham? Ah, yes. Little Master Wareham. Well, you'll grow, no doubt. Your father played rugby, right?'

'For, uh, for, uh . . . for Wellington, Sir.'

'Yes. I remember.' A fleeting grin appeared above the dimple of his receding chin. 'I played for the Wellington reps myself, lad. Fly-half was my position. My job was to outthink the other team and come up with the winning strategies.' He blinked again. Maybe it was a twitch. 'Your father played out on the wing. He was a big fellow, a stout chap. He shoved his way round the field.'

'He was, uh, a champion, uh, sprinter, Sir.'

'A sprinter? Well, yes, he could be surprisingly fast for a big man. And he enjoyed charging at full speed around the field. My goodness, he could be effective, too, sometimes. He could build some momentum and bang into people and bowl them over. But he was a shover, not a strategist. A winger, not a fly-half. Well, strategic thinking was none of his business way out there on the wing. But barge he could, and barge he would.'

So, Coke was a mastermind, not a barging buffoon. But for this weird exchange, you'd have characterised him as vacuous. In fact, the studied nonchalance masked a hyper-competitive athlete, and the lowly gym-teacher role apparently provoked the need to prove himself a thinker. He might lack cerebral gifts and curiosity, but no matter. He was lithe and not unhandsome, and intellectually suited to the pursuit of sporting glory and personal acceptance.

'Now, chaps, for today's dollop of Latin I'm going to enlighten you about what went on in ancient Rome. Back then, just like here in New Zealand today, sports were extremely important, much more so than indoor stuff like plays and music. You hear a lot about Greek and Roman theatre, but, honestly, those were just warm-ups to the big sporting events. Just like the Greeks, the ancient Romans knew that nothing was more important than being fit, so all over their empire they loved their games—riding, fencing, wrestling, throwing and swimming. At home, they played ball before dinner. And, just like modern cricket, those Romans loved to throw a ball as high as possible then catch it before it hit the ground.'

'What about chariot racing, Sir?'

'What about it, boy?'

'I read a book that said the Romans enjoyed it, Sir.'

'Yes, of course. Well, goodness me, absolutely nothing was more important than chariot racing. There'd be a couple of dozen races a day. And just as we look up to our All Blacks, the Romans respected and admired their top chariot drivers. Those riders stood straight up, reins in hand. They wore their team colours, too. And helmets similar to the headgear our forwards wear to protect their ears. The race was seven laps around the stadium—three miles with tight turns at either end of the track—and no lanes and no rules. As the crowd roared it was every man for himself and first to complete was the winner.'

'Were chariot riders as important as gladiators, Sir?'

'Well spoken, boy! Gladiators! Well, those fit fighting men were even more like All Blacks. They fought for glory and they fought to the death. And, just as a coach inspires his team from the sideline, attendants with red-hot irons poked any fighter who was lazy or coasting. And, when a judge decided that a fellow was beaten and should be put out of his misery, that loser would fall to his knees and offer his neck for the winner to cut his throat.'

'That must have been hideous, Sir.'

'Not at all. Gladiatorial schools taught the gladiators how to die gracefully. The loser never screamed or pleaded for mercy. At that point his job was to go quietly.'

'Go quietly into that dark night, Sir?'

'Dark *knights*? No, boy, these were *gladiators*. And the death usually happened in the late afternoon, about the same time that we finish our rep rugby matches. The idea was to depart with dignity. It's the same with rugby and cricket. We hide our feelings from the opposing team. We may be sore and angry, but we don't whine if we lose. We just shake the hands of the opposing team.'

'So it's okay to be a loser, Sir?'

'Not really, boy! Show me a good loser and I'll show you a loser. Winning is the name of the game. We train and train and train—we train until we're fitter than any other team, any other team at all. We train until we drop. We absorb the fundamentals of the game into our blood. Then we hone our skills, sharpen our techniques by practising and practising and practising. Then we study our opponents' game and figure out a way to beat them. We devise a winning strategy and then we break it down into a set of tactics. Then, prior to the match we prepare our minds as we gird our loins. We focus and focus and focus. Then, and only then, proud in the knowledge that we are following in the footsteps of the countless generations of warriors who have gone before us, we stride onto that hallowed turf out there'—moist-eyed he pointed to the field beyond the window—'then we take the field, we enjoin the battle and we immerse ourselves in the glory of the game.' He paused for thirty seconds or so. 'If we lose after all that . . . why then, if we lose . . . if we lose . . . well, defeat might seem bitter in that moment, boys. But the winner wins and the loser learns. Well, if we don't learn we *should* learn. We never let them see that we hated to lose. A real gladiator never lets anyone see that. No, we never show them that. No. We go home and we lick our wounds. Then we come together, we put our minds together, we figure out what went wrong and then we come up with a better strategy for next time. And then we whip 'em!'

'Like you did as fly-half for Wellington, Sir.'

'Exactly, boy.'

Home

'FABAS INDULCET FAMES—hunger sweetens the beans'—Shell grinned—'or so we hope.' You trailed the boarders traipsing across the football field to the College House dining room.

The house master, Mr Cloggenbrau—Cloggs—a congenitally morose fellow, grabbed the big brass bell sitting at the bottom of the stairs in front of the notice board. He swung it like a giant metronome. Piercing peals bounced down the gloomy, tungsten-lit, timber-panelled rooms, corridors and hardwood floors. The boarders lined up in order of seniority around the walls of the boxlike locker room, which also housed a senescent table tennis table. A second blast sounded, and, led by the senior boys, their leather soles drumming the floor and echoing from the walls, you filed into the dining room. Gathering according to their dormitory domiciles, the assembly came to rest at five polished timber tables, each headed by a house prefect.

'For what we are about to receive may the Lord make us truly thankful.' Potts never closed his eyes when saying grace. He dropped to his chair at the large round masters' table set with linen and silver. He was flanked by two assistant house masters and the matron, 'Bandages', so named for the faded, amber varicose vein supports that confined her calves.

Following the first course of parsleyed mincemeat and potatoes,

Potts rose to his feet and tapped his glass for silence. 'Welcome to College House.' His voice was genial. 'Most of you already think of it as home. And I say to you new boys'—he glanced warmly over the newcomer tables—'that it became your home away from home today. We want you to think of it as such, and to be happy here. Isn't that so, Matron?' She nodded morosely. 'And Mister Cloggenbrau'—he waved his hand in Cloggs' direction—'will be watching over you, as will I, too, of course. The book of Ecclesiastes tells us that there is a time for every purpose under heaven. So we want you to work hard and play hard. Rugby, cricket, tennis, table tennis are all good for both body and mind. And billiards'—he pointed to a full-size billiard table in a corner of the room—'can be as good for the soul as poetry and prayer. Money may also be welcome'—he smiled—'so, starting after breakfast tomorrow morning, I will meet each of you in my office and distribute the weekly pocket allowance generously provided by your parents. For now, enjoy Cook's famous treacle trifle.'

Pocket money *and* treacle trifle. Things were looking up. Or so it seemed. Other delights would surely follow.

●

'Did you ever hump a sheep?' George had tucked himself into the bed next to yours.

'Ah, no.'

'I did. Humped my sister, too'—he blinked—'she didn't like it.' His furry upper lip was ripe for a razor. His intellect and sensibility might not have kept apace with his thirteen-year-old frame, but at least he was open-minded and soft-spoken.

Your third-form dormitory housed twelve boys. All were wearing striped pyjamas. All were bouncing barefoot on lumpy mattresses atop slack wires within rickety, timber-framed beds. Potts whisked in. 'Ah, boys! All in our pyjamas, right, lads? Well done. Now we need you all to get into your beds. Master Wareham here is ahead of the game'—he ruffled your hair—'so follow his lead.' A rustle of feet and blankets followed. Potts stepped back into the door and set his slim, nicotine-stained forefinger onto the light switch. 'Lights out at nine. That's the rule, boys.' He flicked the switch and closed the door. As his footsteps faded down the corridor, a full, burning-yellow moon became gloriously apparent. It was framed at the end of the dorm in the tall, wide window that opened onto a steel fire escape. The boys began to whisper apprehensively, but not so the fellow in the corner bed nearest the window. He jumped out of bed and sprang up into the open window. Facing inwards, he hunkered down, and, with the moon casting his shadow down the middle of the dormitory, dropped his pyjama pants, moistened his male member with a generous dollop of saliva, and, moaning gently, set to stroking that generous organ. Faster and faster he pumped. Faster and faster until, staring at the ceiling with his eyes wide shut, a burst of semen shot like an exploding Roman candle into the air. He sat quietly for a moment or two, his forehead as moist as his still erect organ, then stared out into the tomb of wide eyes and gaping mouths. 'That's how we do it, chaps,' he said, wiping himself clean with his pyjama bottoms.

●

'Potts likes the new boys to show an interest in billiards,' said the fourth-former in front of you. As with all College House queues, the pocket-money line proceeded in order of seniority. It passed along the panelled wall of a gloomy corridor that led to a heavy rimu door.

'Yeah,' said his companion. 'Maybe he'll invite you to join his private club.'

You turned the brass bulb handle, pressed the door open and entered. The room was small but inviting. A burst of warmth emanated from sunlight streaming from a picture window that framed the football field and, in the distance, the red brick school building. Potts was seated at a rolltop desk.

'Ah, Master Wareham. Welcome!' His pate shone through the remnant strands of his salt-and-pepper hair, combed neatly backward.

His horn-rimmed, thick lenses suited his face. A narrow set of bookshelves stood beside the window, adjacent to a small sofa, two matching drawing-room chairs, and a bat-wing. A fountain pen lay across an open, blue-lined page within a faux leather volume. 'So your initiation to school rites and rituals went well, Master Wareham? Yes, of course, it did. You're an intelligent boy, destined to accomplish great things in your new home. We're a close family at College House.' His left arm wrapped itself around your shoulder and his forefinger directed your attention the open page. 'See, Master Wareham, recorded for all eternity with royal blue ink, that is *your* name at the top of the page. Pocket money and expenses! Every penny your parents invest in your well-being is recorded in this volume. And, now'—he produced a glistening half-crown coin—'here is your weekly allowance to spend however you choose. Now, see here'—he pointed again to the page— 'watch closely.' His right hand, fresh, pink and manicured, slowly inscribed, in classic English script, the date and the amount, two shillings and six pence. But what was happening with the other hand? Ah yes, soft and supple, it slipped inside your trouser shorts, then lingered on your inner thigh. The soft fingers insinuated themselves into the Y of your new jockey underpants and gently enveloped your tight scrotum.

'I'm off to the dance,' said Von. 'You're running him a bath, Mister Montgomery, and you'll put him to bed—right?'

'Of course, of course.' He watched her disappear into the night, then set his stubby fingers upon your infant shoulders. 'Now, as the bath fills, let me help you out of your pyjamas. Top shirt first—my what a handsome chest! And now, let's loosen that cord so you can step out of your pants. Goodness me, what a boy you are. Is it clean? Let me see. Well, not quite, but soon it will be.'

As you stepped into the bath, he grabbed an ivory cake of Knight's Castille and soaped your nether regions. Soon enough, his fingers had you cleaner than you'd ever been. He dried you, too, taking care to poke in every crevice they could find to fit.

•

'Satan studies you from birth. He knows everything you've said and done and what you do when you think no one's looking. He has assigned cunning demons to tempt you, selecting them according to your greatest weaknesses and their greatest strengths.'

You'd been tossed back into Roman Catholic fires and the whiskey-nosed Irish priest was staring at you. State schools were supposedly non-denominational but effectively Protestant. As a nod to your imagined papist leanings, you were freed from Protestant Sunday services but compelled to attend Roman Catholic Mass.

'Satan promised you pleasure, but you feel alone, guilty and depressed, and you don't know why. You don't know that the Devil's minions have invaded your flesh. They get a bigger piece of you every time you sin. The more frequent the sin, the happier Satan becomes and the more your life goes kerflooey.'

Kerflooey. A lovely, melodious new word. Seemed kind of apt, too. Perhaps this addition to your sensibility might presage even deeper epiphanies to come. Or not.

Strokes

'LAST WEEK YOU LEARNED that each noun belongs to one of the five declensions and one of the three genders. Now, you boy'—he pointed the chalk in his hand at Shell—'what are the six cases in a declension?'

'Nominative, genitive, dative, accusative, ablative and vocative, Sir.'

Wilson nodded. 'Now you in the back there.' He coiled his arm and fired the chalk. 'Pay attention when I'm talking, boy. What is the table for the plural noun, mensa?'

The well-rehearsed reply came quickly. 'Mensa, mensae, mensae, mensam, mensa, mensa, Sir.'

'I said *plural*, boy.' He stared coldly. 'Either you did not learn the plural table, or you were not paying attention. Step to the front of the class.' He retrieved the cane and pointed to the floor. 'Stand here and bend.' He momentarily studied the thin blue trousers on the slim buttocks. 'There will be four strokes, boy.' The words were ice-cold but the strokes were white-hot. As he returned the snake to its resting place, you contemplated the pain-filled footfall of the fellow heading back to his desk. Wilson truly was a critter to be feared.

'Now you, Master Wareham, what is the table for the plural noun, mensa?'

Oh, Christ, no!

'Ah, ah . . .'

'Oh, yes.' He studied your twitching lips. 'So show me your homework.' It was already open on your desk. You pointed to the page and he picked it up. 'Hmm, yes, mensae, mensarum, mensas, mensis, mensis, mensae. Well done, boy.'

His praise brought no comfort. Quite the opposite. You'd always wanted to learn Latin. It seemed a shortcut to becoming a deep thinker. Latin quotes always seemed so wise. Latin seemed exotic to a colonial boy. That was the charm of it. Master Latin and you'd become an educated person. You'd lace your offhand remarks with clever little Latin sayings. People would have to ask you to explain the meaning. You'd be cleverer than them by definition. It would open your eyes to the vibrant world that Romans created. The wars would come alive. The people would come alive. You would come alive. Wilson, alas, seemed not to feel any of that. To him, Latin was a dead language. To you, Wilson was a dead loss. But if he was depressing, the man you were about to meet was not.

●

The scent of photographic chemicals followed the white-aproned storekeeper as he stepped out from behind the black velvet curtain and appeared behind the glass-topped counter.

'Hmm—you have a Leica.' He straightened his canvas darkroom apron, set his elbows on the clear glass counter and steepled his fingers beneath his grey goatee. The overhead fluorescent lit his wide forehead and slate eyes. 'And the classic brown carry-case, too, I see.'

'My, uh, Dad gave it to me.'

'It was a gift?' He pointed a forefinger to the ceiling. 'Lucky boy. A fine camera doesn't make a great photographer, but a Leica lens just might.'

'I, uh, hope so.'

'You're already on your way.'

'I, uh, am?'

'Sure. You're out and about with your camera. The world's your canvas. You only need to take the photo. Until then we have nothing. Nothing but a Leica.' He reached for the camera. As his bony fingers wrapped the case you admired his diamond-studded wedding band. 'A camera sees the world differently than the human brain. Our eyes are scouts on a preliminary search. The camera's eye may change everything.' He opened the case and peered into the lens. 'And this lovely piece of glass might just be a medium through which messages reach us from other worlds.' He smiled, closed the case and passed it back. 'But one needs great film, and great processing too. Are you in pursuit of something special?'

'Just, uh, looking.'

'Just looking? Excellent. The vital component of a camera is the restless mind behind the viewfinder. What kinds of photograph do you like to take?' He raised his palms. 'Don't answer! You like to photograph people—yes? I will indeed take that as a yes. So you take portraits—candid portraits—right?'

'How'd you know?'

'Photography is a perfect medium for one whose mind teems with ideas and imagery. Someone out of the ordinary, as you seem to be.'

'It's just a stutter.'

'So you truly are lucky.'

'Lucky?'

'You see the world through a special lens. It's the making of a great photographer. You don't believe me?' He raised his palms as if to show that he was carrying a gift and grinned ruefully. 'My own blessing is Parkinson's disease.' He set his hands on the glass bench top. 'What I meant earlier was that you are intense and alert, ever on the lookout for the decisive moment.'

'Thanks. What's Parkinson's?'

'A hurry-up call from God.'

'God?'

'Or the universe. You believe in the universe? Yes. So the universe is telling me, and now I'm telling you, to take more photographs, to forever capture fleeting moments of truth.' He reached for your hand. 'Call me Vincent.'

'Uh, sure.' Names and introductions. Always a problem. You hated them.

'Within these walls'—he set his left hand upon your head—'now and forever, your name is Apollo.'

'Apollo?'

'The god of art, light and knowledge.'

●

So the game for Potts was pocket billiards. And he'd paid you the compliment of welcoming you into the club of fellows happy enough— or lonely enough—to play along. Coming so hard on the heels of those choleric English and Maths masters, Potts' empathy was comforting. To be honest, since the Pottsian digits tarried long enough to arouse the male member, the fingering for membership provoked a guilty thrill. But then the hand dropped and, as if nothing had transpired, the basset-hound eyes behind the thick lenses latched onto yours. 'There we are then, Master Wareham.' He pressed the half-crown into the grateful neophyte fingers. 'Off to school with you now. Great adventures lie ahead.'

●

The Leica was small enough to smuggle into classes and focus surreptitiously. The music master was a favourite subject. He was a nice guy, good-looking, neat and well-dressed, soft-spoken, intense—and hopeless. On the bright side, he seemed happy for you to sneak photos of him, in which regard he was not alone.

'Rumour has it that Master Wareham is a shutterbug.' Potts buttonholed you in the College House lobby, just inside the front door. 'And a keen shutterbug, too.'

'Yes, Sir.'

'And you know how to develop film.'

'Yes, Sir.'

'And how to make prints.'

'Yes, Sir.'

'So what you need to ply these skills, to, uh, develop them, one might say, is a darkroom?'

'Yes, Sir.'

'Well step this way, Master Wareham.' He steered you outside onto the front step, and pointed to a narrow door. 'This way, please.' He pushed the door open, led you inside and flipped on the light, a bare bulb hanging from the encroaching underside of the main staircase. 'Might you be capable of converting this janitorial chamber into an official College darkroom?' The space was tiny, dusty and dirty. 'It has a sink, see?' The light danced in his spectacles. 'It's all very grimy, but you could clean it up, I'm sure.'

'Yes, Sir, I could. I really could.'

●

'Ridding your sinful lifestyle is merely the first step to saving your soul from Satan. Now you must go to confession and share a full and forthright accounting of your transgressions. Remember, confession is a sacrament. And when you accept that sacrament, God blesses you. Going to confession is like removing from your foot a nail that you stepped on.'

Silence

THE TROUBLE WITH STUTTERING is that you can never figure out when it's going to fuck up your day. Sometimes, one way or another you can string a sentence together. Other times, all you can do is mouth the air while looking like an idiot. You never know for sure how bad it will be. But some moments are never good. Introducing yourself is hopeless. The Devil has your tongue. That's what new faces see. That's what most of them think, too. Most of them? Maybe so, maybe not. Some look past it. Some see past it, too.

•

'Yes'—Vincent stroked his goatee—'I know exactly where you can acquire usable, second-hand darkroom equipment. And at a very good price, too.'

'I just need a red light and some trays—'

'And an enlarger. No point in a darkroom unless you can enlarge your photographs.'

'I can wait awhile—and my father might help.'

'No need. You've come at the right time. I've been mulling what to do with some old equipment that until this very day I could not bear to part with. Pay for the red light and I'll bequeath everything else.'

'Bequeath?'

'Some years ago my wife insisted I invest in new equipment. I held on to the old stuff for sentimental reasons. We're talking about old trays and an antiquated enlarger. Antique but still excellent for your needs. The lens is perfect. You'll be very happy.'

'I only have to pay for the red light?'

'And the paper and chemicals you'll need to get started. Won't cost much. But I'm guessing that you'll become a regular purchaser of chemicals and paper'—he grinned—'so you'll likely fund my journey into old age.'

●

'So, Johnny'—Von smiled wanly—'I thought I should really tell you myself, before you catch that train back to school tonight'—bad news was on the way—'Chum and I are getting married.'

The world turned.

Tears raced to your eyes.

'Getting married?'

'Tomorrow.'

'Tuesday?'

'At the registry office.'

'Is it too late—?'

'Oh, Johnny'—she reached out and gathered you into her arms—'I thought you might be upset. Chum's not your dad, but he's a good man. You know that.'

You stood silent, feeling like a minor player in a bad movie with no projectionist to halt the reel. You had no choice but to protect her. You could handle truth but she could not. So it seemed, anyway, all the way back then.

Illusions

A SORCERER'S STAR-STUDDED black cone hat caught your eye. It sat above the doorway of a decaying two-storey building two blocks off the town square. Beneath it, wiry lettering spelled out M-A-G-I-C.

As you pressed the door it swung open, revealing a dark corridor and a down staircase. You trod the narrow timber boards and alighted in a tiny, dim basement.

'Looking for a little enchantment?' The mellow voice emanated from the pink lips of a bespectacled, grey-bearded man in his sixties. He was wearing a star-speckled black cloak and a matching wizard's hat, and was standing beneath a modest crystal chandelier and behind the countertop of a showcase containing cards, coins and articles of cellophane-wrapped trickery. Light glinted from one eye but not the other. Perhaps he was sporting some kind of eye-patch. Sensing your puzzlement, he poked a pink forefinger directly into his right eye. 'Lost one of my lenses,' he said, 'but no matter, I still see everything a wizard needs to see. Now, look at these!' He waved his hand over a cluster of posters of illustrious magicians adorning the black, faux-suede wall behind him. 'Would you like to live forever? They used to be famous, now they're immortal. You could be, too.'

'I see Houdini, Ballantine and Thurston, but who're the others?'

'Curiosity! You're an aspiring wizard.'

'I love magic.'

'And all life's mysteries? Mind control, the occult!'

'I had a book on hypnotism once.'

'You wanted to send someone into a trance.'

'Sort of.'

'You wondered what favours the fair sex might bestow when spellbound?'

'I was mainly interested in self-hypnotism.'

'Why so?'

'Well, I, uh, thought it might help with my stutter.'

'I didn't notice a stutter. So it's not much of a problem—or am I wrong?'

'It's okay now, here with you.'

'And it's okay when you conjure for an audience?'

'Well, yes.'

'Aha! I see.'

'See what?'

He produced a burning match from his sleeve and lit a scented candle on the counter. A golden veil rose and spread against the low ceiling. He tossed the dead match into the air, then reached out with an open palm. 'You have a coin? Ah yes! Half-crown, no less.' He held the silver disc aloft. 'Distraction!' His eyes locked onto yours. 'And diversion—voilà! See now—the coin is gone. Magic, my young friend, is the art of misdirection. Your stutter vanishes when you're distracted—just like your disappearing half-crown. Hence your interest in the mystical.'

'I guess.'

'You like poetry, too, right?'

'How'd you know?'

'First, I'm clairvoyant. Second, you're carrying a book of poetry.' He grinned. 'I'll buy it from you. Here's half a crown.' He reached across the counter, and slipped the coin back into the trouser pocket. 'Intuition says you have a problem you'd like to discuss. No? Then perhaps you'd like to make a wish?'

'I wish for some new teachers.'

'Why wish for that?'

'They're beasts.'

'How so?'

'They, uh, beat us.'

'With words?'

'With canes. Drew blood on the boy next to me.'

'Blood? That's not good. That's bad. Really bad—wrong.'

'And that's not all . . .'

'And what?

'Doesn't matter.'

'Really?' He paused and sighed. 'I see.' He sighed again. '*Snakebite!*'

'Huh? What's snakebite?'

'For openers, it's that cane—that lash. It's also the name of a poem. He extracted a dog-eared paper from his cloak and unfolded it. 'Here—"Snakebite"—listen up:

A lash of brightness catches you off guard in childhood . . . that's what happened, right? They filled you with fear—and something else happened, too.'

'Never said so.'

'Might as well have . . . *Now, you swollen and sly, must welcome turmoil as a central friend*'—he paused—'*who plies her fangs of difference through your heart!*' He peered into your eyes. 'Bad things can happen to kids. In the twinkling of an eye you can get bitten by a snake, many snakes, maybe. You're innocent, so you don't quite realise what's happening, nor the harm done. You feel weird but you don't know why. You think you're okay. You go on with your life . . . *You will not understand, but will endure*'—he shot you a glance, and then concluded, softly and slowly, one word at a time—'*snakebit, and never dreaming of a cure.*'

'Is there a cure?'

'There's an antidote. An elixir of magic and courage. The magic begins with honing your gifts and talents, thereby preparing yourself to become the conjurer that your heart tells you is your destiny. As for courage, well, courage is more than virtue. It's the foundation that creates our realities. Courage is using your talents, playing your part in the great drama of life and fully becoming your truest self.' He smiled. 'But that's enough philosophising. Let's turn to what you came here for. Let me help you invest in a magic deck of cards.' He plucked a deck from his cloak. 'This deck is very special.' He fanned the cards. A pair of black snakes wound from corner to corner against a blood red background. 'Pick any card and turn it over. Yes, just like that. Aha, see, the face on what you chose is blank—what does that tell you?'

'That they're all blank.'

'Clever boy. But no.' He closed the fan, then reopened it face side up to show that it was a regular deck. 'You chose the only blank card in the deck. Try again.' He closed the deck, flipped it up, fanned it again and held it out for inspection. This time the snakes were gone.

'How'd you do that?'

'Look again!' He closed and flipped the pack, then spread it face up on the counter. This time all the cards were Jokers. 'Magic!'

'The deck's for sale, right?'

'Yes and no. This is my personal deck.' He gathered and closed the cards, then slipped them back into his cloak. 'But I have another, just the same, on order. It is scheduled to arrive in one week.'

'How much?'

'How much! What earthly value can be assigned to such cards?' I've confided my clairvoyance. Let me also confess that when I woke this morning I foresaw your visit and your need for a magic deck of cards. So, in that moment, by the powers invested within me, the contract was struck and I am therefore delighted to report that you already own the cards.'

'I do?'

'Yes, of course, in the spiritual world they already have your name on them. In the physical world, we just have to wait for them to arrive.'

'How much will, uh, do I owe you?'

'The agreed consideration was half a crown.'

'You want it back?'

'If you have it I will take it. Give it to me now.'

'Holy cow!' Your pocket was empty.

'Magic, my friend, magic!' With a flourish, he produced the coin from the air then offered it across the counter.

'Can't accept it, Mister Wizard—we have a deal, remember.'

'Of course you can! Here, take it. Ah, you trust me! Well, I trust you, too. Secrete that half-crown in a safe place and we'll settle upon delivery when you return. Meantime, as agreed, the deal has been struck'—he shot an enigmatic smile—'and your cards are yours to play.'

The wooden staircase creaked as you gingerly ascended. You replayed the cryptic parting line. You stepped through the battered door into a burst of sunlight. Shading your eyes with the peak of your school cap, you contemplated the time by the post office tower clock. The tarmac was soft beneath your leather soles. Your cards were yours to play.

●

'After ridding your soul of sin with a full, honest, warts-and-all confession, the next step to salvation is to attend Mass every Sunday and to receive Jesus in holy communion, the point where the creator and the created are joined. A truly fervent holy communion helps you fight the demons who manifest as friends and come tempting you to go looking for'—he set two fingers of each hand to his ears to indicate apostrophes—'a good time.'

Visions

'YOU ARE INDEED THE SON OF ZEUS!'
Vincent slowly flicked through your photos.

'I am?'

'Yes—you shoot in monochrome.'

'I like Tri-X.'

'Exactly. It's black and white, moody and grainy. It reveals souls and testifies to time's relentless melt. It has the speed to capture the candid shots you fancy.' He reached back to the wall of multicoloured cartons, extracted a small white cassette box and set it on the counter. His fingertips were tinged yellow from darkroom chemicals. 'Did you ever try Ilford? It's moody like Tri-X but not so grainy, creates a softer, deeper image. Not many people use Ilford, so it can give your work a special look.'

'Like Man Ray?'

'Man Ray! That youthful alchemist forever seeking the photographer's philosopher's stone. Is that what you aspire to?'

'I guess.'

'May you never find it!'

'Why not?'

'It would end your experimenting.'

'What should I, uh—'

'First, never forget that you are irreplaceable. Your life cannot be repeated. So your quest is as unique as your chance to pursue it.'

'Second?'

'Trust your own vision and create your own style.'

●

'Godly souls seeking truth and happiness in this life and salvation in the next need look no further than the Catholic Bible. But it does not always mean what *you* think. No! It has one meaning only. The Holy Roman Catholic Church, which is the originator of the Bible, in union with God, the author, is the one true interpreter. Jesus sent the Holy Spirit to guide the Church in Truth. So, on every page, so long as we heed the Church's interpretations, we are guided by the Holy Trinity.'

●

'Match point,' called Potts. Surprisingly, given his disinterest in other sports, he'd appointed himself scorekeeper. You watched in awe. So tonight did the other sixty boarders, jammed around both sides of the table. The air was warm and sweaty, the atmosphere electric. How did these guys get to be so good at table tennis? This was not mere Ping-Pong. This was spectacular, speedy and special. The victor would be College House champion.

The favourite, Gloyn, was up two sets. Though only a fifth-former, he seemed a certain winner. A steady and stylish player, he kept the ball in play, waiting for the right moment to unleash his flick backhand and win the point. His upper-sixth-form opponent, a more popular fellow, was a first-rate player but marginally outclassed. The rallies were long and the game was close. The white celluloid globe shot back and forth. Maybe Omar played table tennis:

The ball no question makes of ayes and noes,
But right or left as strikes the player goes;

And he that toss'd thee down into the field,
  He knows about it all—he knows—he knows!

'Match to Master Gloyn'—Potts smiled amiably—'whom I formally declare to be house champion.'

The players shook hands and the applause was generous.

This was the game for you.

But what about Potts? You felt a burst of shame, not for anything you'd done, but, now, for what you knew you had to do.

Weekends

YOU GATHERED Tubby and Smallman into a dark corner of the empty reading room.

'Potts recruited you guys, uh, right?'

'The pocket billiards club?' said Tubby.

'Yeah, we signed up,' said Smallman. 'So what's up?'

'We gotta, uh, close it down.'

'Out, out! Get that cheating cardsharp—that fucking little dwarf—out of the house.' The shouting woke you. Chum had gotten himself caught dealing from the bottom of the deck. They, whoever it was, chased him out the door and up the street.

The decision to sacrifice the Joker did not come easily. Potts was warm, gentle and good-humoured—he often switched lunchtime grace for a snippet of poetry. But when you heard he'd shared his Saturday night bed with Raven, a sunny, mischievous fourth-former, you knew he'd gone too far.

But tell the whole truth. You also felt betrayed. You'd imagined you were the special one. Now, however, it was hideously clear that these two were well and truly into each other.

'You wanna snitch on Potts?'

'You're gonna turn him in?'

Their faces showed less shock than surprise.

'The sooner the better. He bedded Raven. You wanna wind up there?'

They glanced into each other's eyes, then back.

'Potts is top College House wallah—who can we tell?'

'No matter what you say, they won't believe you,' said Tubby.

'If three of us pipe up they will.'

Tubby grinned. 'He took Raven in the, uh, weak end?'

'Up the weak end.'

Humour heralds deepest truth,
crack the grin that's burglar proof,
pull the rotting wisdom tooth,
release the shadow from the youth.

As you peered through the half-open headmaster's door, Peggy, eyes glued to his Bible, mouthed the reading for the imminent morning assembly. You tapped the oak and he glanced up. 'You boys have something to report?' he said softly.

You pushed the door open. 'Yes, Sir.' You were weirdly fluent.

He glanced at his watch. 'Time is short, and time is flying, boys— but come right in.' You entered the office, closed the door and stepped onto his Persian rug. 'So what is it then, that brings me face to face with three of our finest citizens?'

You glanced at the others. It was all go.

'We need to report a problem, Sir.'

'Well then—you've come to the right place.' He stepped out from behind his desk and waved his hand over the slim floral guest sofa in the corner of the room. 'Make yourselves comfortable'—he settled into a facing chair—'and speak your piece with all due haste.'

'It's about Potts, uh, I mean, Mister Stowe, Sir. We just call him Potts.'

Peggy touched his nose, stroked his wispy moustache and studied you. 'And what is it about Mister Stowe?'

In one minute there are moments for decisions and revisions which a minute will reverse. This was not such a time. No matter your ambivalence, no matter your affection for the only teacher who seemed to possess a decent heart, no matter your feelings of complicity and shame—and no matter the guilty sense that you were about to grass a courteous, considerate and civilised fellow, this was indeed the moment to do just that.

'We like him, Sir, but he, uh, touches us.'

'He, uh, Potts, uh, that is to say, Mister Stowe, uh'—the sharp eyes momentarily glazed over—'he, uh, touches you?' The silence was palpable. 'All of you—ah, I mean the three of you? Yes, that's a yes, right? But, how, precisely—uh, I mean, where, precisely, might he have touched you?'

'He runs his hand up our trouser legs, Sir.'

Peggy mulled those words.

'Up your trousers? I see. I think I do. But, ah, where might he, ah, stop?'

'He doesn't stop, Sir. He touches our private parts.'

'Your private parts? Your *private* parts!'

Tubby clenched his fist. 'He grabbed my cock, Sir—when I was getting my pocket money—stroked it, too.'

'This happened to each of you?'

'Yes, Sir—and others.'

'We called it the pocket billiards club, Sir,' said Smallman.

'And he buggered Raven!' said Tubby: 'Got 'im in the weak end.'

You watched the words spill onto the open page. Were they your words? Yes. But where had they come from? And where might this poem end?

The runner never moves;
he rests his feet
on racing earth
and the world turns.

Dragons and Maggots

PEGGY STRODE DIRECTLY to the lectern. Summoning a level of gravitas not previously apparent, he cleared his throat and launched into the homily.

'Today's reading is from the Book of Isaiah. "I form the light, and create darkness: I make peace, and create evil: I the Lord do all these things."' He peered over the lectern. 'Evil exists because God gave us free will, the freedom to act rightly or wrongly. He gave us that choice because it is the wellspring of the only kind of love, goodness or joy worth having. God knew that bad things would happen if we made the wrong choices, but he judged it worth the risk—and so must we. This is not to say that we must accept evil. No, not at all. Our duty is to defeat evil.

'And so, in the course of life we each confront a series of challenges. If we knew for sure who was evil and who was not, we could isolate and destroy them. But what does a dragon inside its shell look like? We cannot know, for when we break the shell the dragon is no longer to be seen. And so it is with evil, whose nature is to hide in the darkness. Shadows and darkness are intrinsic to our existence. To remove the shadows would be to destroy our very selves. Darkness is everywhere. When we walk in the midday sun the darkness is fastened to the soles of our shoes. People are neither good nor evil, only their acts. It is not monsters who commit monstrous acts. Darkness dwells within even the best of us. Only in the worst of us does it reign.

'The Devil has power to assume a myriad of pleasing human shapes, all of whom go nowhere uninvited. They share our homes and dine at our tables. The Devil has no book, parable or proverb that tells us how to be bad. Human beings are perfectly capable of evil all by themselves. The line separating good and evil passes through every human heart. It is a shifting, wavering line, yet even in a heart subjugated by evil, a stepping- stone of good remains. And even in the best of all hearts, an evil seed resides in a dark corner.

'When we confront wrongdoing, we come face to face with the need to act. If we fail to fight evil, we champion it. Evil cannot be purged, but so long as we fight it—so long as we reproach and punish evildoers—it can be contained. An impure impulse is infinitely less evil than an intentionally immoral act, for that is the conscious choice of evil. It is the wilful evasion of knowledge, and the deliberate suspension of sight and of thought. It is a maggot in the soul.

'All evil begins with the belief that another's existence is less precious than one's own. Corrupt people are mostly unaware of their venality. Evil invades when we're not paying attention. Passion can blind us and lead us to sin. We are all flawed, so a transgression that arises from a sudden passion may be pardonable. But anyone who transgresses with premeditation has cast his eye on the law, on the punishment and on the consequence thereof to human society—all of which, in committing the crime, he holds in contempt as lesser than his own appetite.

'To secretly act contrary to professed principles, to live profanely, incontinently or irreligiously, is a greater defect in a teacher than a child. Such sinners not only commit crime, they also teach it to others.

'Morality demands vigilance and reinforcement. There is good in the worst of us and evil in the best of us, so we must develop and maintain the capacity to forgive. To be unable to forgive is to smother the power to love. To forgive evil is not to excuse or tolerate it. We look it full in the face, call it for what it is and let its horror shock, stun and enrage us. Only then do we forgive. In so doing, we conquer the power of evil to dishearten us, for in that moment we remember that nothing can happen that God hasn't allowed. Even resistance is all part of a grand orchestration. The Devil always has you right where God wants you.'

●

You caught a glimpse of Potts from the window of the mid-morning maths class. He strode across the football field as if pursued by the Devil, yet still managed to seem poised, not daring to reveal fear, even to Beelzebub. Books and papers were clamped beneath his elbow. His fists were tight, his eyes steadfastly downcast, as if contemplating that the clay beneath his feet might open and swallow him. He pulled the door open and disappeared inside. You felt a thud in your heart as it closed behind him. The rumour ran that he'd been booked on the next plane to Australia, where his bent might pass unnoticed.

●

At lunchtime, Cloggs stood behind Potts' chair and delivered a guttural grace. 'Father of us all, thank you for saving us. This meal is a sign of your love for us. Bless us and bless our food, and help us to give you glory each day through Jesus Christ our Lord. Amen.' He waited for everyone to be seated, then continued in his trademark mangled English. 'For reasons personal, no longer with us is Mister Stowe, so for the balance of the term his duties I will overtake.' A murmur followed. 'Change is part of life yet accords with God's plan always.' He gazed to the ceiling and back. 'Two sides there are to every issue. Right is one and wrong is the other. But the middle is evil always. If he accepts the responsibility of choice, the wrong man may be a good man. But the middle man is a knave. Truth and choice do not exist, he says. Willing he is to sit out any battle, to cash in on the blood of the innocent or to crawl on his belly to the guilty. Conflicts he solves by ordering the thinker and the fool halfway to meet. In any compromise between food and poison, only death can win. Only evil profits in any compromise between good and evil. In that transfusion of blood which drains the good to feed the evil, the compromise is the transmitting rubber tube. Whoever from God's Word strays, goeth to the slaughter like an ox, or the stocks like a correction to the fool.'

Hey, God, bring back Potts! But there it was. If there's a god, he'd grabbed your cards, rigged the game and pulled you into his divine plan. That's how this fellow said it works. And as soon enough became apparent, in the know he might have been.

Truth

'SO THEN'—his eyes popped as he gripped the pulpit—'for many, being a sinner is a natural human state of existence. It is also the pathway to hell. It also creates a hellish life in the here and now.'

I neutered the verb
and disowned the declension,
and my case, alas,
will defy redemption.

'Nil desperandum,' said Shell. It's only first term Latin so it will be a simple exam. Just reread the exercises and look over the answers we gave and the translations we made. Then, when you get into the room just give it your best effort. You mightn't top the class, but an acceptable grade is on the way.'

The answers *we* gave and the translations *we* made? In fact you'd merely copied Shell's work. Sure, you survived for thirteen weeks. Wilson administered the lash to others, but never to you. Why would he? Everything you turned in was perfect. But the moment of truth was at hand.

Uh, uh! Don't like the look of this:

Alexander the Great fulfils a prophecy in an unusual way thanks to the cleverness of a mule driver. Translate into English:

Olim Alexander, rex Macedonum, cum exercitu suo ad terras Indorum iter faciebat. certo die haruspex ad regem venit. ille haruspex, postquam dixerat regem in magno periculo esse, eum quoque monuit ut, si diu vivere vellet, occidi iuberet eum qui primus sibi, ex porta egresso, occurrisset. itaque Alexander imperavit ut milites asinarium, qui forte regi ante omnes alios obviam ivit, caperent et ad mortem ducerent. sic sperabat se praeceptum haruspicis perfecturum esse. asinarius autem quaerebat cur rex eum innocentem poena tam gravi puniret. Alexander igitur illi dixit quid haruspex monuisset. quibus verbis auditis, asinarius inquit: 'si ita est, rex, praeceptum haruspicis alium, non me, huic morti destinavit; nam asellus quem ego ante me agebam prior tibi occurrit.' Alexander, cum haec verba callida audiverat, tam laetus erat ut asellum, non asinarium, interfici iuberet. hoc modo Alexander praebuit se regem sapientissimum esse.

It was all Greek to you.

•

The sorcerer's hat was gone. *FORTUNES TOLD*, the sign now said. You descended the staircase and stepped inside. In the middle of the bare, dim room, a crystal ball on a gold stand sat on a round table covered with a star-encrusted black cloth. Incense wafted from a corner pot.

'I have a visitor?' It was a woman's voice. You turned. 'A *young* visitor.' She'd stepped through a gold door set within red-and-black taffeta walls. She looked like Von, but her skin was almost as sallow as her yellow headband. She smoothed her blue silk gown, then tapped her golden earrings. 'The fates have sent you to know what lies ahead?'

'I, uh, was looking for—'

'The magician's gone.'

'Gone?'

'What's that you have there? Half a crown!'

'We had a contract.'

'A contract? Wonderful! He's been called elsewhere, but the agreement shall be satisfied.' She plucked the coin from your hand. 'All contracts are spiritual. Come sit, the universe wants us to talk, so talk we must.'

Her hands were soft. She studied your face. 'We see a home that is unhappy—yes? Yes. We see a young man who feels cut adrift. He is talented and curious. He seeks answers to eternal mysteries. He is unafraid to go where his heart leads him. But that heart is troubled— yes? Yes. And he is lonely now, yes? Yes. As to the future, we see him in troubling situations—yes? We see him struggling. And fighting. And winning—yes!'

'Do you have any, uh—'

'Advice? Yes. You are here today to discover the answer to a question. The elucidation will complete your half-crown contract. What is the question?'

'How can I, uh, fix my, uh, stutter?'

She closed her eyes, squeezed both your hands and sat stock still. Seconds passed. 'I am listening to the universe'—she let your hands drop and set her palms to the table—'and it has spoken clearly.' She peered into your eyes. ' "Why bother?" That's what the universe says. But wait, I hear more.' She closed her eyes. ' "Where you stumble, there lies your treasure." Yes! Suffering is a gift. We must turn our pain into riches.'

'But how?' You waited patiently.

'For now, our contract is complete.'

Rude Awakenings

'HERE, I GOT IT—SEE!' The groping of your dick was unbidden and unwelcome. It happened on the first day of the new year. Other than for this gawky goon, you were alone in your new dormitory, changing into your school uniform. He'd propped himself on the bed next to yours and waited for the decisive moment. 'You've never pulled yourself off?' He encircled you with his left arm, imprisoned your back close to his chest, and pumped your member hotly and madly within his right clenched palm. You fought to break free. 'Oh, you want me to stop?' He paused. 'One head is trying to say yes'—his coarse face was staring into yours—'but this other head down here'—he tightened his grip—'is definitely saying no.' He pumped faster, almost vengefully. 'Oh, stop it, I *like* it,' he sniggered. 'Stop it, I *like* it! Stop it, I *like* it!' He threw you aside and jumped to his feet. Peeved that his affections had been rebuffed, he stalked to the door. You did not care to watch him depart. 'At least you now know how to pull yourself off.' The door clicked shut. You studied the newly polished floor, then slowly raised your eyes. The beds were neat and sun was streaming in the window. Everything all looked okay. But everything was not okay. This encounter was more depressing than the sum of all such others. But why? Perhaps because this was the beginning of a new year. Perhaps because such a loathsome creature had so wantonly unseeded you. Yes, sure, he had indeed shown how you might create more pleasure for yourself, albeit all too fleeting, than you'd previously imagined possible. And, yes, once again the violation that exposed your vulnerability also made you tougher. Or so it seemed.

●

'The Burning Bush! The Book of Exodus tells us that it suddenly and mysteriously flamed alight and burned intensely—yet never died. It was a light to the world. It was a fiery revelation. God himself shone from within those flames.'

You personally never got to peek at such a bush. Following your rude arousal, however, you became familiar with the burning pubis, the steel stick that it stoked, and the tight, white-hot compound it made of your scrotum. This was a burning indeed, an inflammation to be reckoned with, a heat that drove young men into each other's arms. It was the lust that dare not speak its name. To sate that fire in the midnight hours that year, you shared sheets with a like-minded lonely soul. Well, perhaps not so much like-minded as caught in the same carnal trap. A handsome, young farm boy, more gifted in sports than academics, a realist not a dreamer. What you had in common was a burning in the bushes. Such guilty delight. Come morning, though, no mention was made, no look was passed. Absolutely nothing had happened, or so it seemed.

IDEAL MARRIAGE: Its Physiology and Technique *by TH. H. Van de Velde. This book can do more to lessen conjugal unhappiness than all the religious exhortations from Moses to Manning—Harry Elmer Barnes, New York World-Telegram.* Whitcombes has books on everything. You picked it up and flipped it open. *The wife must be taught, not only how to behave in coitus, but above all, what and how to feel in this unique act.* Interesting. Hence *Part III. Sexual Intercourse; Its Physiology and Technique.* This was good advice, surely. *Varieties of Erotic Kiss. The*

Tongue Kiss. The Body Kiss. The Love-Bite. The Sensations of the Bitten Partner. Mammary Stimulation. Diagrams, too. And an index. 372 pages in total. Interesting.

•

'The devil'—he pointed his forefinger to the floor—'has no power over us unless we succumb to his temptations. So we have two choices'—he raised both digits—'and two choices only.' He panned the assembly. 'We either nurture our souls and thereby raise our bodies to heaven'— he pointed the fingers like pistol barrels—'or we permit our carnal lusts to drag our souls down into the everlasting flames of hell.' He clenched his hands into fists and held them alongside his copious pink ears. 'Choose wisely.'

•

'Do I squeeze your knackers again, or will you jump?' Ginger, his mop of red hair flashing above his freckle-faced smirk, had his naked victim by the testicles and was pushing him backwards along the mildewed board towards the acrid waters of the grungy, concrete, above-ground swimming baths.

'Yeah, Jump! Jump! Make the bugger jump,' shouted the sallow-faced fifth-former Coyle. It was a numbing scene, as unreal and depressing as a bad movie. Coyle was a hero to some but never to you.

After dinner and prep, boarding boys were permitted to sojourn there, just a couple of hundred yards away from College House, for a refreshing dip. The pool was surrounded by a six-foot corrugated iron fence adorned with a peeling coat of bile-green paint. An uneven set of concrete steps led through a rickety gate. Inside the enclosure, a narrow wall of open-plan changing sheds, protected by a rusting iron roof, overlooked the murky twenty-five-by-six-yard pool, wrapped within a six-foot concrete pavement.

What happened within this gloomy space was hidden from outside view, but once inside the walls all privacy was lost and everything happened in plain sight.

Ginger's voice was menacing. His emasculations were equal parts verbal and physical. He was small for a bully, but thickset, cunning and creative.

'Now! Jump, c'mon—NOW! What's the fucking holdup?' He grinned at the pun. 'The holdup! Hey, Coyle! Is *this* the holdup?' Coyle laughed as Ginger squeezed the testicles and pushed the shivering victim to stand tiptoe, precariously balanced at the extreme edge of the board, contemplating the chlorinated liquid, yellow by the light of an early moon, six feet beneath his terror-filled eyes. If he were to jump, would Ginger hold on or let go? Would manhood be forever lost? It was impossible to tell. That was the conundrum.

Cruelty was pretty much the norm, so survival was everything. Turning in Potts was easy. He had broken the law. His behaviour was criminal. Ginger and Coyle were infinitely more cunning. Only a fool would run foul of them. Others laughed along but mainly out of fear. Most tried to pretend that nothing unusual was happening, which was true. This level of boyish horseplay was one of their favourite entertainments. To give either of them cause to suspect that one might turn him in would be to invite the wrath of fully-fledged sadists, confident and assured in their cruelties. To be fair, they were both okay students. And, on the rugby field, their intimidating ways could be helpful, especially in a rugby scrum when supposedly raking for a ball. Severely injured members of opposing teams emerged from such mêlées, but coaches seemed not to notice. In their presence, they both adeptly tempered their sarcasm into a mollifying, jaunty, one-of-the-boys humour. They were, to be sure, sly devils.

Crusades

A BRIGHT SUN warmed your closed eyelids. It was morning break. You were sitting between Ted and Shell on a quadrangle bench in front of the old wooden gym. You felt a shadow block the glow. 'Are you chaps serious about your lives?' The earnest voice belonged to Upton Wright, your sometime platoon leader. 'I mean, really serious?'

'I'm serious about cricket practice,' said Ted.

'I try not to be serious when relaxing,' said Shell.

'Uh, why?'

'Why am I asking?' Upton clasped his hands together. 'Because something serious is happening at quarter to four tomorrow afternoon in the physics laboratory.'

'There's trouble?' said Ted.

'Not at all'—Upton pulled his interlocked fingers to his chest— 'quite the opposite. An American scientist is passing through town and has agreed to share some insights with us.'

'Us—who's us?'

'It's not a school thing, Johnny. Not really. Peggy just lets us use the room. We're the Crusaders. We're a gathering of fellows who really are serious about tapping our talents.'

'Will it help me get into the first eleven?'

'Crusaders do their best in every sphere, including sport. And we help others do the same. But we're humble, too, we never boast or skite.'

'What kind of science does this fellow teach?'

'Physics. He uses it to show how nature affects our destinies.'

'Is it like the Boy Scouts, with badges and things?'

'We believe in deeds, not ornaments. Listen, chaps, you don't have to be a Crusader to attend the meeting. You only have to be serious about life. So come and see if you like what the fellow has to say. He might show a movie, too.'

'I've got cricket practice—how long's it gonna last?'

'A movie?'

●

So did that wretched stutter shape your life? *Yes.* And *No.* You felt frustration, not depression. But maybe you're lying. What about the poems you hoped might turn your pain to riches?

> *The wound, the tender flesh, the weal,*
> *the bleeding mind that feels*
> *the scarlet scar that never heals;*
> *the scab torn fifty times a day.*
> *Why feed on me, you bird of prey?*
> *Why tug my tongue for your buffet?*
> *Why peck upon the heart's sachet?*
> *One of us, with death must pay.*

Okay, yes, you thought about giving up. But how, exactly? A gun would do it, but where would you get one? And what about all that blood? Same thing with a razor to the wrists. Poison would be painful. Hanging? No thanks. Too slow—and what if you change your mind while swinging in the air? You could jump from a building. The descent might just be the experience of a lifetime. Again, though, what if you have second thoughts halfway down? Anyway, there were no tall buildings in Palmerston. You'd have to wait until you got to Wellington. Lots of opportunities there. Something to think about. Maybe this American scientist can make everything go away, the problem and the cure both.

Moon Madness

SEVENTY CHAPS CRAMMED into the physics laboratory. You and Shell were in the back. Upton was perched within a phalanx of friends in the front row. The agricultural master, Mr Clay—Mudd to most—was seated alongside a beaming fortyish fellow in an immaculate, grey gabardine suit.

Clutching a piece of paper, Mudd stood and gathered his battered gown around him. 'We salute our leaders for their spiritual guidance. I am honoured to introduce Doctor Irwin A. Moon, who has been called "The Million Volt Man" for reasons that will soon become apparent. We are delighted to present this'—he smiled—'electrifying speaker— pun intended, chaps!—to our Crusader gathering'—his eyes sought you out—'and to all seekers of truth and salvation.'

Dr Moon rose, his bearing poised, his face alert, his forehead high, his blue shirt and tie perfectly complementing the custom-tailored suit.

'What a joy for me to speak to you here in this beautiful, unspoiled town today.' The voice was silky smooth. 'Recent discoveries of modern science have ended the age of materialism.' The pitch and pacing were hypnotic, mesmerising even, for the classroom seemed to disappear, and with it every other person, except yourself and the good Doctor.

'Many people seem to have two compartments in their brain, Johnny.' His eyes were warm, the smile a winner. 'They have faith in science on one side of the brain, and faith in religious teaching on the other—and, fearing that science will sweep away religion, they set an immovable wall between them. *But only faith founded on truth can survive.*'

'Well said, Sir.'

'Thanks, Johnny. Did you ever see a million volts of electricity? No? So now you will!' Like a wizard tossing stardust, he waved his hand and you blinked. The room seemed brighter. 'We can use this equipment'—he pointed behind him to the instrument-laden wall, and, in front of it, an electrical transformer the size of a desk—'to produce a million volts right here and now.'

'Wow!'

'But what has that to do with faith, Johnny? *Nothing*—not if faith is a retreat from fact. *But,* if faith is founded on fact, then the million volts and everything in this laboratory has a *vital* connection. Hence'—he drew a tiny Bible from his vest pocket and read from a well-thumbed page—'Jesus said to Nicodemus, "*except a man be born again* he cannot see the Kingdom of God." Now, that sure mystified Nicodemus. "How can a grown man be born again?" he asked. Well, Jesus gave him a *big* answer. He must be born of the *spirit*! Ah, yes, said Jesus, "the wind bloweth where it listeth, and thou hearest the sound thereof, but canst not tell whence it cometh, and whither it goeth: so is everyone that is born of the Spirit."'

'I love the King James lines, Doctor Moon, but I'm wondering how they relate to science?'

'Good question, Johnny. You're a kindred truth-seeker. So from now on just call me Doc.'

'Really?'

'Sure. Now here are the facts. There are two worlds all around us: the physical'—he paused—'and the *spiritual*. But before we can see or enter this spiritual world we must *change*. We must undergo a virtual rebirth.'

'These are facts?'

'Faith, Johnny—stay with me.' He excitedly described a bunch of natural wonders, birds migrating to weird places, fish swimming upstream, that sort of thing. 'These are cases from the physical realm, Johnny. And biblical examples demonstrate the reality of the spiritual world.'

'The Bible's historically accurate?'

'Sure is, Johnny. And in Genesis we find God and man in perfect harmony. These two worlds are one. But then man sinned. So God withdrew and set between us an invisible barrier. It stayed in place until God stepped across the barrier and became Jesus Christ, *thereby creating a way that we can cross back and return to him!*'

'Do we know how he did this, exactly?'

'What we know, Johnny'—now he sounded a tad testy—'is that Jesus lived on earth, died on a cross, and was taken down and entombed. Then Saint Peter went to Christ's tomb and saw that Christ had miraculously vanished from within hundreds of yards of wrappings. He had *risen from the dead.*'

"But how, exactly?"

'Don't you get it Johnny? It happened because Jesus' body was *spiritual.*'

'The earthly body just disappeared?'

'Yes, Johnny—yes! How that happened is only a mystery to the, uh, *un*-reborn. You seem confused, so let me *show* you *exactly* what happens.' He produced a magnet and two metal strips from his pocket. 'This steel strip clings to the magnet—see? And this brass strip does not!'

'So?'

'Physical forces can be selective in their effect. Watch!' He removed his shoes and sprang up onto the electrical transformer. 'Now, Johnny'— he extracted from his vest pocket a bunch of metal thimbles—'I have ten of these little caps and, as you see, I'm putting one on each finger and thumb.' He smiled proudly. 'And now I am going to permit a million volts to pass through my body and out through my fingertips.' He pointed his thimbled fingers to the ceiling. 'So kindly step forward and hit that big red switch.'

'You sure?'

'Just do it,' he said, 'for it is not my life that is at stake, but your immortal soul.'

You hit the switch and impressive streaks of lightning shot in all directions from his fingertips. 'Off now, Johnny. Thanks. Inspiring, right? Now, I'm removing the metal caps from my fingertips, see? So this time pass me that thick cane beside the transformer.' You did and he held it aloft in his right hand. 'Power on, Johnny.' The cane burst into flame. 'Power off!' He jumped down, tossed the smouldering stick into the waste bin, removed and restored the thimbles to his pocket, then pulled his shoes back on. '*That's* what I'm talking about! Spirituality is just like that. Just as a wall of invisibility separates man from God, the power passed through me but set the cane alight. So Christ wasn't kidding when he said we must be born again. And *that* is the message of this sacred book.'

'But aren't we going around in circles, Doc? I mean, isn't the Book of Genesis open to countless interpretations?'

'*God* says, you must be born again, Johnny.' His eyes glazed over. 'How can we be born again? *This book*'—he hoisted it aloft—'*has the answer.*'

'I love the idea of switching in and out of spiritual worlds, Doc, but don't we need more proof than electricity and a book?'

The room began to spin and you blinked. As you opened your eyes the million-volt machine faded back into a blackboard.

You felt a sharp pain in your side. Shell's elbow was in your ribs. You blinked. Doctor Moon, calm and collected, pearly-gate smile patched between his lips, was holding forth to seventy pairs of upturned eyes.

'You are at the crossroads between time and eternity. Why don't you take the omnipotent God at his word? *Now* is the time to come to Jesus.'

Descents

'LEADERS CAN BE treacherous and corrupt,' Twaddle peered over his horn-rimmed glasses. You came last in English, maths and Latin—no surprise there. What a relief to get kicked down to the B-stream. Oh happy day! No more Soapy or Grubby. Twaddle—his actual name—was the English master. 'And heroes can be villains.'

Twaddle was a great teacher, intellectual expectations were lower, and everything was more relaxed. The physical environment, a draughty, makeshift, shanty building with wood-burning stove-heaters, was a downgrade, but no one cared. Those pot bellies gave off real warmth and smelled good, too.

The idea that leaders could be double-dealers got your attention. Maybe you could learn something about Potts and Cloggs. Or Soapy, Grubby, Gus and Coke. You set your elbows on the desk, propped your head in your hands and opened your ears.

'Cassius cunningly persuades Brutus to join a plot to kill his close friend, Julius Caesar, Emperor of Rome. First he strokes Brutus's ego:

Tis just. And it is very much lamented, Brutus,

—It's too bad, Brutus—

That you have no such mirrors as will turn

Your hidden worthiness into your eye
That you might see your shadow

'Yes, it's too bad for you, Brutus, that you don't have any mirrors that could show you what a great guy you truly are!' Twaddle raises his spectacles and grins. 'You see what a cunning fellow Cassius is—right, chaps? You there, Master Wareham—you're getting this, am I right?'

'Yes, Sir. Yes indeed.'

'So now Cassius presses on, cunning as ever, suggesting that the Romans want Brutus to lead them.

I have heard
Where many of the best respect in Rome,

I've been listening to the town's top wallahs

Except immortal Caesar,

But not Caesar—he's still in the dark about all this.

talking in hushed tones about you, Brutus
And groaning underneath this age's yoke,
And complaining about the tyranny of today's government
Have wished that noble Brutus had his eyes.
and wishing that your eyes were working better.

'So Brutus is being gulled and can't see it, Sir?'

Twaddle's eyes lit up. 'Right indeed, Master Wareham!' He smiled, happy to have found a kindred spirit. 'And now he deftly mocks not just Caesar, but also the followers and friends who put him on a pedestal:

Why, man, he doth bestride the narrow world
Like a Colossus, and we petty men
Walk under his huge legs and peep about
To find ourselves dishonourable graves.

'And now, even more cunningly, Cassius tells Brutus to do more than think—now is the time for action, he says. Now is the time for your star to rise, your name to be on everyone's lips:

Men at some time are masters of their fates.
The fault, dear Brutus, is not in our stars
But in ourselves, that we are underlings.

'An underling! He's telling Brutus that he's an underling. And that he, Brutus—not the stars or destiny—is to blame for that sorry state. He's telling Brutus—the second most powerful man in Rome—to buck up and become a master of his own fate.' Twaddle pushes his spectacles back onto his ruddy forehead and stretches out his arms, palms upward. 'Can you believe the nerve of this fellow called Cassius, chaps?' He said chaps, but he was looking at you. The others were gazing blankly. 'And he doesn't stop there!'

Brutus and Caesar—what should be in that 'Caesar'?
Why should that name be sounded more than yours?
Write them together, yours is as fair a name.
Sound them, it doth become the mouth as well.
Weigh them, it is as heavy. Conjure with 'em

'He's seized upon the thing that men like Brutus hold most dear—their name!' Thumbs tucked into his Harris tweed vest, Twaddle strutted back and forth across the room. 'He's telling Brutus that his name should be on everyone's lips. Before our very eyes, chaps, a good and decent man is being corrupted—and tragedy will follow!' He abruptly stops. 'Do I have that right, Master Wareham?'

●

'You've been dodging and burning, Apollo.' He smiled. 'I don't just mean dodging classes and burning the midnight oil.' He pointed to your photo prints. 'I'm talking about darkroom magic. Lightening and darkening parts of an image.'

'Yes, of course.'

'These are very good—'

'But?'

'The blacks should be jet black, the whites pure white. Your blacks are grey and your whites are misty.'

'What's the fix?'

'Paying closer attention. Becoming aware of the elements that a great artist hides in plain sight. Now you see it, now you don't. You see what the photographer wants you to see, you see the *subject*. But when we fully see the subject we also become blind to the magic that went into the bigger picture.' He glanced at his wobbling fingers. 'Life, Apollo! Light and shade. Light today, darkness tonight. Spring today, winter tomorrow. We need to pay attention, but the very act of living—of savouring a special moment—causes us to miss the bigger picture.' He peered into your eyes. 'Am I confusing you?'

'Not really.'

'Not really? Great.'

'Great?'

'Of course, for we have now engaged a process.'

'What happens next?'

'Life goes on, but is never the same.'

●

'Marlon Brando's coming to town'—Ted was incredulous—'and we're gonna miss cricket to meet him?'

'He's agreed to open the batting.'

'Johnny's joshing. In fact, a movie of Shakespeare's *Julius Caesar* is coming to town. Brando is merely among the dramatis personae.'

'But we're gonna miss cricket?'

'Ars longa vita brevis.'

'Huh?'

'Art is long, life is brief.'

'It's a long movie?'

'The sight of Brando in a toga may inflame a love of all things aesthetic,' said Shell. 'Our mentors hope to inspire respect for the Swan of Avon by exposing us to the sinews of the lad from Brooklyn. The cast also includes James Mason, John Gielgud and Deborah Kerr. Brando the mumbler, Mason the mellifluous, Gielgud the ingratiating and Kerr the elocutionist. Each has something to teach.'

'Says you.'

●

'Architectura est musica gelida, chaps.' There you were, stuck in the middle as the entire student body pressed like a fat python through cage-like doors of the Regent theatre. Shell was on a roll. 'Architecture is frozen music, chaps. So remove your caps as we pass through this splendid art deco monument.' You trod the lush carpet and filed through the oak-lined lobby. 'We're Philistines in most things, but at least one Kiwi understood that the noble life demands noble architecture.'

'Arty theatres enrich the experience?'

'Of course.'

'And sell movie tickets?'

'Whatever sells is art.'

Rubbernecking the softly lit chandeliers, you scaled the grand staircase to the mezzanine floor, crammed your uniformed bodies into the serene space and peered below. Ted nudged you. 'Are you seeing what I'm seeing?'

'Yes.'

The headmistress of the Girls High School had also cottoned on to the academic value of the Brando-Bard matchup. In the dim light beneath five hundred pairs of lusty male eyes, mysterious and sexy in their black stockings and smocks, lay the full, warm complement of Girls High maidens.

'I wouldn't crawl over any of them to get to you.'

'They're here for Brando, not us.'

'They're panting for lights to go out.'

Such base thoughts were banished by chords of the national anthem, and the Technicolor image of the becrowned, bejewelled, young and radiant Empress of the British Commonwealth. You enjoined the piping of your leaders and begged God to ensure that the noble queen enjoyed a long reign and a glorious life.

The dirge finished and the gathering fell back into the faux-leather seating. Shell, leaning on his wooden armrest, turned to you. 'Nunc ante oculus Caesar cupidate non adulatione percussit occidit,' he whispered.

'Huh?'

'Caesar will now be stabbed to death for craving precisely that kind of royal adulation.'

●

Thick and wet and surly grey.
A cloudy sky, a murky day.
An asphalt street, a gravel tray.
You really need to get away.

A forlorn gathering of spine-challenged classic novels and a stained *Everyman's Encyclopaedia* huddled within a shaky bookcase in the darkest corner of the dining room. But there was a bright spot. Potts had vanished but the popular culture he favoured had not. He'd subscribed to a happy assortment of magazines including *Life* and *Look*, and British imitations. They sat in a pile at the end of a long table with bench seating. On the all too many rainy days you perused the eclectic mix of Americana, royals at play, moody photo-journalism and gossipy feature stories. Happily the British fondness for scandal peppered the pages. Of special interest was a series of feature articles on Alistair Crowley, the Cambridge-educated Briton who dedicated his life to evil, as a particularly weird studio head shot made clear. He was sporting a shaven bald head atop occultish robes, while clutching his slippery skull between closed fists and glaring back into the camera. What was the message of his bulging orbs? What was the meaning of his overblown poems? And what about these ink drawings? They really did conjure an apprehension of authentic evil. He'd also persuaded a lovely acolyte with a helmet haircut to permit him to brand her with a red-hot poker. The swastika-like image neatly balanced between her appealing breasts was something to ponder.

> *'The occult is a demonic gateway through which Satan and his minions invade your soul. Too many sinners open that portal by reading their daily horoscope, playing with ouija boards or having their fortunes told by so-called psychics. These preternatural pursuits can seem like harmless fun but they are dangerous games. Your soul is at stake and the outcome has been rigged not just by the Devil, but by his minions, too. The more you commit yourself to Christ, the more demons Satan assigns to you to trap you. Fall into their net and there's only one way out. Confess to a priest, then sprinkle any occultic object with holy water and burn it. Your life will become a living hell if you do not.'*

●

Might your stutter have turned your life into a living hell? Not really. Purgatory perhaps. Or intermittent torture. Here it comes again:

Mouth locked
Tongue blocked
Not shocked
Mask mocked

For sure, the erratic nature of the infliction could deliver dollops of embarrassment, perhaps even shame. But you could hide all that:

Dayshine
bright
eyeshine
gulp and grin
and let me be.

Happily, if some fellows mocked the impediment they did so behind your back. Perhaps they imagined you enjoyed demonic powers. Or maybe they feared the defensive lash of sarcasm that most stutterers develop. The tongue might not lasso but at least it could be made to whip. Moving on was easier said than done, though:

> *It's easing now*
> *this crimson pain.*
> *The scarlet*
> *scar remains.*

•

'You are reading *what*?' Cloggs' cold grey eyes appeared above the page. You closed the magazine and engaged his stare.

'Just, uh, looking, Sir.'

He grabbed the magazine and flicked slowly through the pages, his head nodding, his lip curling.

'Nothing wholesome I see here. You are Roman Catholic. In this school a good example you must set.'

This school. You knew what he meant. You were both outsiders. Him more than you, actually. You were merely an observer from another planet.

'I must?'

'Yes.' He was about to leave but changed his mind, sorted the magazines into two piles, tucked one stack under his arm and slid out of the room.

'Quod factum est?' Shell's voice was a whisper. 'What happened?'

'It's all gone!'

'What's gone?'

'Anything worth reading. He took it.'

'Maybe he's reading it in his room. That stuff on Crowley was really interesting. He was a bright man and a great linguist.'

'You liked him because he knew Latin?'

'He also studied philosophy and literature at Trinity College, published poetry and lost his virginity to a family maid on his mother's bed! The maid got fired and became a homeless drunk. Then Jack the Ripper cut her throat.'

'Wasn't that just a rumour?'

'For sure Crowley was into black magic.'

'The occult.'

'Yeah. Joined the Hermetic Order of the Golden Dawn but got expelled for being a homo.'

'Most of those guys were.'

'He was flagrant and insatiable. That's what peeved them. He went for everything. Alcohol and drugs, men and women, prostitutes and rent boys, even animals. He wound up in a miserable deathbed. When his doctor refused to prescribe the morphine he wanted he put a curse on the quack and they both died hours later!' Shell shrugged. 'I guess he was true to his credo—'

' "Do what thou wilt shall be the whole of the law." It's a big idea—'

'What'll Cloggs make of it?'

'If he reads it, he'll burn it. He's a true believer. He fears for our souls. Timendi causa est nescire.'

'Huh?'

'Ignorance is the cause of fear.'

●

If masturbation was a necessary evil, table tennis was an addictive panacea. You played before and after breakfast, before and after lunch, after school and before dinner, after dinner and before prep, then after prep and before bedtime. You bought the paddle endorsed by world champion Victor Barna and a book with action photos of heroic world players. You relentlessly practised the signature Barna backhand flick. You got good at the game. Others suffered the same addiction. Finding keen competitors capable of beating you—and thereby raising your game—was seldom a problem and always a quest. Losing would lead to winning, surely.

Twaddle, beaming broadly, strode into the classroom. 'So, what did we think of the movie?'

'Better than expected, Sir.'

'Anyone else?'

'Would've been better with less talk and more action.'

'The words got in the way?' Twaddle grinned. 'What'd you think, Master Wareham?'

'Caesar was, uh, kind of deaf, Sir.'

'How so?'

'Didn't, uh, listen to the, uh, soothsayer.'

'And?'

'Or connect him to Deborah Kerr's dream—'

'You mean Calpurnia—Caesar's wife—not Deborah Kerr, the actress.'

'Yes, Sir.'

'And you noticed, I'm sure, that as Caesar enters the Capitol, one of his supporters cautions him to trust nobody.'

'Yes, Sir.'

'So why did Caesar not heed these warnings?'

'Didn't listen, Sir?'

Twaddle strode to the blackboard and grabbed a chalk. 'Remember this word, chaps—hubris!' He scrawled it on the board. 'It's a deadly mix of overconfidence, arrogance and pride.'

'Pride goeth before a fall, Sir?'

'The first lesson of this play is that hubris blinds and tragedy follows. Hubris causes leaders to cast aside common sense. Caesar's intuitions were sound, but hubris led him to ignore them.' He tossed the chalk into the air, then watched it fall back into his pink palm. 'The second lesson is that people are not always what they seem. We know from the outset that Cassius is two-faced. Caesar knows it, too. But Brutus, the man Caesar regards as a close friend, stabs him to death. And Mark Antony, who seems a hero, riles up the crowd and sends them to war—

then drops his voice and says to himself—and us—"mischief thou are now afoot, do thou what thou wilt." '

'So Brando's a villain, Sir?'

'Mark Antony, Master Wareham, is a *man*. He is capable, as we all are, of anything.'

●

'A surprise this is,' said Cloggs, feigning a smile. The dour subtext of his mangled clauses was never much in doubt. It was the last day of the school year. You would head home in the morning. 'Top in English, you came?' Overjoyed he did not seem. 'Also mathematics?' If he tried to block your ascension he failed. You got kicked back up into A-stream.

That night, as you lay mulling what might lie ahead—wherein your drowsy fears proved prescient indeed—notes from a soft-pedalled, midnight piano came a-gently-tapping at your eardrums. Yes— it was the mysterious Moonlight Sonata. And, yes, it was coming from Cloggs' private chambers. Seems he owned a well-tempered clavier. He also had a nice soft touch on the keys. You pushed back the bed covers, set your bare feet onto the cold floorboards, trod softly to the door, opened it, stepped out into the corridor and followed the music.

His door was slightly ajar. Through the crack, six flames flickered from a candelabra atop a handsome upright piano. He was seated back to the door and wearing a scarlet silk robe. As the sonata ended, he lowered his hands and glanced back over his shoulder and your eyes locked. But no—and why were you not surprised? The bulging orbs within this bald bullet-head did not belong to Cloggs. Plucking a lavender handkerchief from his pocket, the Great Beast wiped a layer of perspiration from his brow, then stepped his fleshy frame to the door and opened it.

'Ah, Master Wareham'—his voice was dulcet—'we've been expecting you, do come in.' We've been expecting you? 'Yes, *we*,

Johnny, You don't mind if I call you Johnny, do you?' He pointed to the corner of the room behind the door. Cloggs in his striped pyjamas, wide-eyed, gagged and hog-tied with his own sheets, peered up from the floor. A petite, hand-carved crucifix hung at eye level on the wall behind him. 'Had to do it, Johnny. He's an ass in need of education. We must help him see beyond his own silly schnozzel.' He bent down and tweaked the Cloggs nose. 'Isn't that so, Mister Zealot?'

It all seemed pretty natural. And an opportunity not to be missed. 'An honour to meet you, Mister Crowley—I mean, you are Mister Crowley, right?'

'Well, yes. But if you don't mind, I'm a devil, so I'd prefer you call me Great Beast—Six-Sixty-Six would be okay, too.'

He pointed to an upright cane chair opposite the piano stool and swivelled his chair to face it.

'Sure, but which is the surname and which is the Christian name?'

'Oh, please, Johnny! Those are my given names. I gave them to myself.' He set his right elbow into his left hand, and rested his chin on his right hand. 'The universe has brought us both together in this funny little room—and in the presence of this dense Dutchman—so I'm presuming, even though I mostly prefer the symphony of silence, that we have things to discuss'—he half-smiled—'though I must confess that words, most people's anyway, are mostly as wasteful as they are untrue.'

'But in serious discussions, isn't talking the same as thinking?'

'People believe that talking is a sign of thinking, Johnny. But talking is mostly a mechanical dodge of the body to relieve oneself of the strain of thinking—just as exercising the muscles helps the body to become temporarily unconscious of its weight, its pain, its weariness and the foreknowledge of its doom.'

'Wow, that's crackerjack! No wonder you call yourself the Great Beast. Did you figure that out yourself?'

'People tried to tell me things, but real knowledge comes from within.' Faint fumes rose from the flickering candles behind his bullet-head. 'The mark of the untrained mind, as witness this ass on the floor, is the assumption that its own processes are valid for all men, and that its own judgements represent absolute truth.' He waved his hand in Cloggs' direction. 'Idiots like this were always insisting that I memorise what I did not understand. But being first-rate, my memory refused to be so insulted.' He tilted his nose, inhaled the scent of the candles and smiled at the soft moans emanating from Cloggs. 'I tell you, Johnny, for this dense ass to look at a mountain would be like an illiterate confronting a Greek manuscript.'

'He seems to disagree.'

'Do I care? His intolerance is testament to his impotence. What he needs to know—what just about everyone needs to know, actually—is that it is an unpardonable sin to wilfully reject truth, to fear knowledge that does not pander to prejudice.'

'But how would you teach him anything then?'

'Well, first, keep in mind that everyone interprets everything in terms of his own experience, so if you say anything that doesn't touch a precisely similar spot in another man's brain'—he glanced at Cloggs— 'he either misunderstands you, or doesn't understand you at all.'

'Sure, but how can we convey the truth to someone like him, then?'

'Oh, Truth's a fickle whore, Johnny. This ass thinks she belongs to him alone—everybody does—but she cheats on everyone. A single ego is an absurdly narrow vantage-point from which to view the world.' He smiled. 'But you want a serious answer, right? So listen. Balance every thought with its opposition'—he raised his forefinger—'because the marriage of opposite thoughts is the destruction of illusion.'

'Hey, that's great! I love it. So religion's an illusion? And faith's a big mistake?'

'Of course! I speak from hard-won experience, Johnny. I slept with Faith and found a corpse in my arms on awakening.'

'Wow! How did you deal with that?'

'I went back and drank and danced all night with Doubt—and found her a virgin in the morning! Listen, Johnny. You go mad if you take the Bible seriously'—he grinned—'but to take it seriously you must be already mad!' He chuckled. 'And all this talk about suffering humanity. It's drivel based on the mistake of projecting our needs to our neighbours. The so-called Golden Rule is okay in theory but hopeless in practice. In fact, the supreme satisfaction is to be able to despise one's neighbour. That's a fact. It explains religious intolerance, the great consolation of imagining the people next door are headed for hell.'

'But isn't your own creed, "Do what thou wilt", isn't that a kind of religion, too?'

'No. The true man of genius deliberately subordinates himself, reduces himself to a negative and allows his genius to play through him as it will. In the absence of willpower, the most complete collection of virtues and talents is worthless. The eternal mistake of mankind is to set attainable ideals. Pure will, on the other hand, bereft of purpose, is in every way perfect. The joy of life consists in exercising one's animalism, always growing and changing and always enjoying every new experience—to stop is to die.'

'But following personal wishes, wants and desires often upsets other people.'

'Ordinary morality is for ordinary people, Johnny. Modern morality and manners suppress all natural instincts, keep people ignorant of the facts of nature and make them fighting drunk on bogey tales. A man's friends can do him more harm than strangers. But his greatest danger lies in his own ingrained habits. It's a terrible mistake to let any natural impulse stagnate. Crush it out, if you will, and be done with it. Or fulfil it and get it out of the system. But never allow it to remain and putrefy.'

'Putrefy? How?'

'For openers, suppression of the normal sex instinct causes a thousand ills. Puritan countries are morbidly preoccupied with sex and every form of perversion.'

'So, if I have it right, the goal is to escape all this, uh, evil—'

'Evil is the wrong word, Johnny. Conformism is the right one. Evil is good, conformism is bad. Evil is the solution, conformism is the problem.'

'Yes, of course! But how do I actually go about applying the Do What You Wilt doctrine?'

'First, bear in mind that it is necessary, in this world, to be made of harder stuff than one's environment. Speaking for myself, I've never outgrown the supposedly infantile belief that the universe was made for me to suck. The key to joy is disobedience. The Way of Mastery is to break all the rules—but you have to know them before you can transcend them. So keep on acquiring a taste for what is naturally repugnant. That is an unfailing source of ultimate pleasure. We conquer life by living it to the full. Only then can we meet death with aplomb and prestige.'

'But what about love? Isn't that what makes life worthwhile?'

'Doubtful, Johnny, doubtful. The few love affairs which came my way were silly and sordid. They brought no bliss. It was a vastly overrated pleasure, a brief and brutal blindness. Boredom and disgust came hard on its heels. That said, I must also confess that I got great pleasure from unbridled sex with a like-minded disciple.'

'Unbridled sex? How does that work?'

'The hour is late, Johnny. But let me share this poem about the experience.' He fell into a curious, snorty, sing-song voice:

She was the harlot that shaketh death.
I was the shaker that giveth the peace of satiate lust.
Immortality jetteth from my skull,
and music from her vulva.

What awful poetry. No wonder he didn't give up on his beastly day job. But you kept a straight face.

Immortality jetteth from her vulva also,
for her Whoredom was a sweet scent,
like a seven-stringed instrument
played unto God the Invisible, the all-ruler,
that goeth along giving the shrill scream of orgasm.

So bad! But those big brown eyes were looking for praise. What to say?

'Amazing! Only a great beast like yourself could have put that poem together, Six-Sixty-Six.'

'Thanks, Johnny. But the night is fleeing fast. I need to take my leave with a solemn blessing.' He stepped to the crucifix and inverted it. 'Now let us kneel.' He grabbed Cloggs by his pyjamas and set him on his knees, mouth to the floor, butt to the ceiling. You knelt, facing the Beast. He raised his hands, pressed his palms together and lowered his purple eyelids.

'Oh, Great Satan,' he intoned, 'invest our young acolyte, Johnny, with the valour to swear off every kind of virtue, so that he may triumph even when he falls. Give him the wisdom to understand that the meaning of life is that it ends, the courage to succumb to temptation and the strength to pursue, share and sate all of his deepest desires and basest lusts.' The eyelids rose, and the eyes shone. 'And, now, Johnny, desire is upon me, so I must heed that call.' As in a tango, he flung his scarlet robe open and tore the pyjama pants from the upended Dutchman. Mounting the poor fellow with practised aplomb, he grabbed a clump of Cloggs' hair, raked his gagged head backwards and shot you a glance. 'Ah, Johnny, I never tire of the pleasure of bringing sensitivity to otherwise insensitive asses.' Eyes gleaming, he put his moist mouth to Cloggs' ear. 'Some men are born sodomites,' he cried, as with a sledgehammer thrust he penetrated the reluctant dyke. 'And some achieve sodomy—ah, yes, ah yes!' He pumped savagely, his teeth reflecting the flickering candelabra. 'And some have sodomy thrust upon them.'

Moving forward

'OPEN UP, JOHNNY, I have big news!' That was Shell rapping at the darkroom door. You spent a lot of time there after Cloggs burned the Crowley magazines and cancelled anything else worth reading. You were finishing up for the day, so this visit was well-timed. You opened the door and Shell stepped inside.

'Let me guess. Cloggs got us a five-year subscription for *National Geographic*?'

'No! The news, well, the rumour actually, is that Cloggs is on the way out and the cavalry is coming!'

'He's been fired?'

'He was only a fill-in. He's been replaced.'

'Who's it gonna be?'

●

'You will agree, then. My example has been righteous in this time of modification.' Cloggs closed his tenure as College House head and slid back into his seat at the round, silver-laid, white-linened, lunchtime dining table.

Coke stepped up into the silence, glanced in the direction of the big boys at the sixth-form table and pushed his hands together. 'Let's hear a big thank you for Mister Cloggenbrau, chaps. He gave you his best, by golly he did, yes.' Cloggs, deadpan, folded his linen napkin. 'Well now chaps, as you just heard, I have accepted the appointment to be your new house master'—he tightened his grip on the back of his chair and beamed—'and Missus Colquhoun will take on the role of matron.' All glances fell upon the petite woman seated by his side. She smiled back at everyone—*for* everyone, actually. This was Betty. She was thirtyish and pretty, and her smile was lovely.

'Now, as you know, when I captained the Wellington representative rugby team, I played fly-half and was the master tactician. And that's the role I intend to play as house master.' His nasal accent had been promoted to colonel. 'I can figure out what we need to do, but for follow-through I need to be able to depend on you chaps'—he glanced first to the prefects, then over the room—'the senior boys and you the younger chaps, too. We'll need discipline and teamwork. What does that mean? Well, these days, as most of you know, in addition to coaching school teams, I'm also wicketkeeper for Central Districts'— he glanced vacantly in the direction of the fields beyond the windows— 'and some say I might be selected to play cricket for New Zealand.' He lingered on that thought. 'But that will take drive, dedication and discipline.' He refocused. 'I have the drive and I have the dedication.' His eyes rested on our upturned faces. 'So what I need is what we all need—discipline. Now, I'm going to deliver, by golly, but what about you fellows? Well, winning is all about pressing on with sweat in your hair and cramp in your gut, chaps. It's about never giving up. It's about staying the course and winning the day.'

'What'dja make of that?'
'Coke's happy to be numero uno.'
'Of a fifty-boy boarding house?'
'It's a step up from gym teacher. And he'll be more enchanting than Cloggs.'
'We might get some magazines back?'
'Sports gear, cricket pads and protective boxes.'

'What'dja make of Betty?'

'Bella est! She's a peach.' He dropped his voice to a whisper. 'But no kids—Coke fell on a crossbar and crushed his testicles.'

'Huh!' It was hard to hold that thought and not feel pain. Or to ponder what it might be like to bed her. Confess it, Johnny, you thought about that often.

'That's the rumour.'

'Maybe she'll mother us.'

●

'They strung him up! They really did. Vindicta est naturalis, et dulcis!'

'Huh?'

'Vengeance is natural and sweet. They strung him up!'

'Strung him up? Who?'

'Soapy.'

'Whattaya mean, strung him up? And who did it?'

'It was a going-away present on the last day of the term. A bunch of our biggest sixteen-year-olds bagged him. They're old enough to quit school and that's what they've done. But first they bundled him into the cloakroom. They stuffed a bamboo pole through the sleeve of his suit all the way out the other side.'

'They turned him into a scarecrow?'

'Kind of. They'd waited for him. It was payback. He'd whipped one too many. They hung the two ends of the pole on the coat hooks. He couldn't get out of his suit and his feet couldn't touch the ground.'

'They crucified him?'

'It was a neat piece of stagecraft. I'm guessing the pole was symbolic. They left him there, twitching and blubbering. Seems he puddled the floor, too. Smelt bad, they said.'

'Who'd they tell?'

'Dunno, just heard a bunch of guys talking about it. Guess someone let the cat out of the bag.'

'How come no one heard him blubbering?'

'Most everyone was off watching the Old Boys' cricket match.'

'There'll be hell to pay.'

'Don't think so. They're out of here and they're never coming back. Soapy won't want anyone to know. Nobody will, you'll see.'

●

Hey, the black cone hat! That was him there, calmly sitting on a bench in the town square. You skipped across the road.

'Can I ask you a question?'

'A good question could help us both.'

'Is it okay to seek revenge—or to be happy that someone did?'

'That's two questions.' He smiled and the black hat turned to scarlet.

'Hey, how'd you do that?'

'Revenge has a life of its own, and colours to match.'

'It just goes off and does things?'

'Magicians can help it along. To exact revenge is a duty. Two wrongs might not make a right, but in the hands of an accomplished sorcerer they can strike a perfect balance and set things aright.'

'How does that work?'

'Some say there's no justice, only revenge. I say we should forgive our enemies'—he grinned—'but not before we hang them.' He pointed a finger to the sky. 'And then we must bring them back to life.' The trick hat turned royal blue.

'Bring them back?'

'It's easier than you think. Revenge is the ultimate illusion. The taste is sweet but the aftertaste is bitter. It begins in anger but ends in pity. We imagine we see an all-powerful torturer, but then the curtain drops to reveal a tormented weakling.'

'How long does that take?'

'Patience lends magic to vengeance. Beware the fury of the patient magician.' The hat turned firehouse red. '"You may have tied my hands," he says, "but my mental powers will soon enough cause the universe to unloosen them. When I get the chance to pay you back, I will. I'll wave the silk of calculation. The universe will transform my hot quest for vengeance into a cold and delicious dish."'

'*You* can do that?'

'The universe helps. Balance is the order of things. It may take time, but revenge always arrives.'

'But it's okay to hurry it along?'

The hat turned gold.

'The best revenge is to be unlike your torturer.'

'They hung this guy from the cloakroom hooks. Aren't they just like him?'

'If the only way to balance the universe is to injure someone, we shouldn't leave ourselves fearing their vengeance. Either cripple them for life or get even while remaining invisible.'

'What about turning the other cheek?'

'I believe in the magic of realism. Ultimate magic is ultimate reality. Nothing inspires forgiveness quite like revenge. The power of revenge lies in the magic of the forgiveness that follows. Not forgiving is like drinking rat poison, then waiting for the rat to die. Forgiving is not about absolving evil. It is about finding the words that change us from victims to survivors.'

●

Ted raced into the room clutching his buttocks. 'Wilson beat us—all of us!'

'All? Who's all?'

'A bunch of us, a hundred or so. We were waiting at the main gate to see the first fifteen get on the bus to Napier. We weren't meant to be there. But it's a big match and we wanted to give them a decent sendoff. Then Wilson caught us.'

'And?'

'He ordered us into the quad?'

'All of you—a hundred!'

'Yes.'

'Then?'

'Then he made each of us bend over for two strokes. Wicked they were. Christ it hurt—here, look!' Ted turned and dropped his trousers. 'Nasty, right?'

'Yeah.' The crimson welts, fresh and angry, seemed almost to be weird living creatures. What to say? 'He got you on the thigh, too.'

'He's not always a straight shooter. Can lay it on your back sometimes.'

'He did that to *everyone?*'

'Yeah'—his lip trembled—'said he had to teach us a lesson.' Ted gingerly raised his trousers and tightened his belt. 'Maybe he just wanted to toughen us up'—his grin was shaky—'mentally as well physically. I mean, that's what matters, right?'

'Spare the rod and spoil the child?' said Shell. 'I doubt that kindness caused this callousness. Seneca says that cruelty springs from weakness—ab imbecillitate omnem crudelitatem. The worst thing is that these wretched masters do it with a good conscience. Moralists love such brutishness. It's why they invented Hell.'

Guts and glory

'SO, SIR,' SAID COYLE, oiling his tongue, 'what was the most important thing you learned playing fly-half for Wellington?'

It was late Friday evening. A bunch of admirers had formed a circle around Coke. Arms crossed, he was warming his butt against the yellow enamel of the coal-fuelled kitchen ovens.

'That's hard to say, boy.' He eyed Coyle fondly. 'I learned many things. Let me see now.' They could've been mistaken for father and son. Both were olive-skinned and swarthy. Both attempted to obscure humble origins with a veil of condescension:

> . . . *lowliness is young ambition's ladder,*
> *whereto the climber-upward turns his face;*
> *but when he once attains the upmost round*
> *he then unto the ladder turns his back,*
> *looks in the clouds, scorning the base degrees*
> *by which he did ascend.*

'Ah, yes! The most valuable thing I learned was to think like a winner.'

'Think like a winner, Sir. Yes, of course.'

Ginger nodded. 'Showing you mean business, Sir?'

'Exactly! Thinking like a winner and showing you mean business.'

'Rugby's not a game for sissies, Sir?'

'It is a game for men, Runting. It develops manhood and confidence and pride. To play the game is to enjoin a struggle for superiority and a battle of wits. We need brains'—he pointed a forefinger to his temple and tapped his stomach with his fist—'and we need guts.'

'No guts no glory, Sir?'

'Right again, boy!' Coke ruffled Ginger's chestnut mane. 'You're a tough little bugger, Runting.'

●

'Do you remember how you loved some of your first photos?'

'Yes.'

'Do you still love them?'

'These new ones are better.'

'Our first ten thousand photographs are our worst. After that we can start to judge them with a cool eye. Let me look closely now. Ah yes—much improvement!'

He smiled warmly and you felt good.

●

'Can we help you, young man?' What she meant was, 'It's mid-morning, why aren't you at school?"

'Researching, Ma'am—a school, uh, project.'

'I see. What subject?'

'Religion.'

'Religion. Hmmm.' She studied you closely. 'Dewey decimal section 200 to 300 in aisle five—over there.'

A public library is a living graveyard. Wander among the shelves to wherever the fancy takes you, grab a book, crack it open and resurrect a mind from the past. What about this Rosicrucian manual? Didn't you see an advertisement somewhere to send off for a correspondence course they run? No need now. Wow, this is exactly the stuff you can never find. Seems the Rosicrucians made a careful study of life's mysteries and figured some things out. Pictures and drawings, too. Interesting. Very interesting. That fusty librarian shot you a weird look. Maybe she discovered you don't have library card.

A burst of sun hit the railroad that ran through the middle of the town, separating the library from the post office. A weak but insistent bell broke the ghost-town silence and the railroad gates descended. You nursed the Rosicrucian manual beneath your jersey. Two chimes sounded and you glanced at the round white face of the post office clock. Half past ten already. What to do? Okay, it's not actually a ghost town. Just feels like one. And here comes the train. On the way to Wellington, no doubt. A cloud of steam rose from the engine. It felt good and it smelled good. The ground thundered as the carriages rolled past. You waited, then watched the last goods wagon disappear through gardens within the town square. The bell stopped ringing and the gates ascended. You crossed the street, wandered into the square and found a seat in the sun beneath the shade of an imported palm tree.

'Like the cat in the tree, getting caught up in the chase can leave us in an awkward place.' The voice was melodic. You glanced up. The mouth was framed by a neat goatee, and two bright eyes peered through small, round, silver-rimmed lenses. There seemed no harm in talking to him.

'Hey, that's kind of poetic—are you a poet?'

'It's a famous Rosicrucian poem.' He smiled. He seemed old but kind of ageless, too. 'Couldn't help but notice you immersing yourself in our secrets, so I thought you might like the poem.'

Our secrets. Did he really say that?

'Well, I just got it from the library. I don't really know much about the subject. I mean, *Rosicrucian*—what's all that about, exactly?'

'It's a mystical order. I founded it in an earlier life.'

'*You* founded the Rosicrucians?'

'Sure, we took my name, Christian Rosencreutz.' He seemed serious, not at all crazy. 'I was born in 1378, the last member of an assassinated German noble family.'

'You escaped and now you're a ghost?'

He smiled, engagingly. 'Do I look like a ghost?'

'Not really'—you contemplated the crimson tie and the gold watch chain in the waistcoat of his charcoal pin-stripe suit—'not at all, actually.'

'Then we're both on the same cosmic plane.'

'How does that work, exactly?'

'First let me answer your question. I was hidden in a monastery. As a young man I wandered through the Near East. I learned the mystical wisdom of the Arabs and Egyptians and became enlightened.'

'Was that helpful?'

'Less than you'd think. When I went back home to share what I'd learned, the townsfolk just laughed.'

'You were a prophet without honour in your own country?'

'I found a few like-minded friends, eight of us actually, all bachelors and virgins, and we formed the Fraternity of the Rose Cross.'

Oh, God, no. *Bachelors and virgins.* Was he just another dogma-ridden priest?

'Did you have a creed?'

'Not really. Well, kind of. We agreed to become healers and request no payment. We wanted to be regular citizens, too, so we had no special vestments or uniforms.'

'Sounds good. Did you have any rules?'

'We met each year at our temple or sent a note to explain our absence. We had a seal, but it was simple, just the letters C.R.'

'That was it?'

'We agreed that each of us would recruit a successor.'

'And it really was a secret brotherhood, right?'

'Yes.'

'So how come you advertise? And how come we're even talking?'

'Ah, well, we only agreed to keep it secret for a hundred years.

And we still don't ask people to join. Not explicitly. We just tell our members to watch out for those in tune with our thinking.'

'Thanks for saying we're on the same cosmic plane, but what might it take for me to become fully enlightened?'

'First, we'd need you to sign up.'

'You won't tell me now?'

'First we'll need a commitment.'

'You can't tell me anything?'

'We could if we wished. We could spread enlightenment, enrich the whole world and release it from innumerable miseries. Rosicrucian history stretches back to Pharaoh Thutmose III in 1477 BC—and it includes anyone who used more than three per cent of their brain.'

'Three per cent—is that a lot or a little?'

'Rosicrucians include Leonardo da Vinci, Isaac Newton, Pascal, Spinoza and Francis Bacon. But we're never manifested and made known unto any man, without the special pleasure of God.'

'I'll need a nod from God?'

'You'll need for God to see that you're on his side.'

'After that, what would I learn, exactly?'

'In your first five years as a Rosicrucian, you'll cover the three neophyte degrees.'

'There are *three* neophyte degrees?'

'Of course—First Atrium through Third Atrium.'

'Then what?'

'Then the temple section—First Temple Degree through Ninth Temple Degree.'

'*Nine* temple degrees? What would I know then?'

'We'll be covering mental alchemy, telepathy, telekinesis, vibroturgy, radiesthesia, cosmic protection, mystical regeneration and, of course, attunement with the cosmic consciousness.'

'I thought I was attuned already. I mean you said we're on the same cosmic plane, right?'

'At this moment you and I have been called together, but you'll need to complete the degrees to become fully attuned to the cosmic consciousness.'

'*Called together*? How does that work?'

'Our Council of Solace also offers magical help to troubled Rosicrucians and serious seekers of truth, which is what seems to be in play.'

'What sort of troubles?'

'Money, home, health, depression, those kinds of things.'

'How does the cure work, exactly?'

'The Council puts spiritual energies into motion and directs them in accordance with mystical law and natural principles.' He paused. 'You have some troubles you'd like some help with?'

'Well, yes—my stutter, for openers.'

'I didn't notice a stutter.'

'I'm okay here with you, but it can be really depressing at school.'

'How depressing?'

'I can be totally honest?'

'Of course.'

'I sometimes feel like just, uh, ending everything.'

'Oh, my dear boy. Oh dear, dear, dear.' He clasped his hands together. 'But I'm delighted you've shared this, uh, concern. Our apparently chance meeting now makes perfect sense.'

'It does?'

'Cosmic forces are in play. You've manifested me.'

'I have?'

'Absolutely. I don't exist on an earthly plane. My body is lying in a geometrically proportioned cave, incorrupt, and bathed in white light from an unseen source.'

'But you truly are here right now—and if you're not, then who'm I talking to?'

'Well, yes, *you* can see and hear me.' He stood and waved his arm over the town square. 'But you're the only person here who can.'

'*I'm* delusional?'

'Not at all. Merely troubled. And your distress has tapped you into the Council of Solace.'

'Wires got crossed?'

'Something mystical happened, Johnny.' He sat back down and peered closely into your eyes. 'It has us on a mission.'

'We're on a joint mission?'

'Your part might now be complete. You have manifested me and shared a secret. My role is to share Rosicrucian wisdom concerning the act of suicide.'

'You have a position on this?'

'We not only advise against it, we say that it is impossible.'

'But it happens all the time.'

'Not really. Worldly life is not an ultimate end. To die is not a decision that belongs to man.'

'It's not?'

'Not at all. Death is merely a natural transition. Death will come when it comes, but where others see a death, we acknowledge a continuity, never a rupture. Man can intervene in his existence only by acting to prolong, for as long as possible, the existence of his instrument, the body. Rosicrucians never attempt suicide.'

'What if they had a terrible stutter?'

'If subjected to immense physical or moral distress, a troubled mortal can, if the Council of Solace does not intervene, come to an act of such extremity. But that is an exceptional case. It does not change the principle that no authentic seeker of wisdom can terminate his existence in this world. A materialist, imagining that death is an end, might commit such an act. But an authentic spiritualist, for whom the body is the temple of the soul, endeavours to maintain it in good health. A true seeker, as you clearly are, wants to live well and acquire the wisdom necessary to make a difference in the world.'

A faint chime sounded. 'Tempus fugit, Johnny!' He tugged his watch chain, extracted a golden fob watch and flicked it open. 'Our mission is complete, so I'll be leaving now.' He sprang to his feet. 'But let me depart as I began—'

'You have another poem?
'How did you know?'

From cycle to cycle, through time, and through space,
Your lives with your longings will ever keep pace.
And all you that you ask for, and all you desire,
Will come at your bidding, as flames out of fire.

'This is a happy note to depart on.'
'I'm not quite finished—'

You are your own devil, you are your own god.
You fashioned the paths that your footsteps have trod:
And no one can save you from error or sin,
Until you shall hark to the spirit within.

Chimes began to peal. You glanced to the post office clock. It was noon. When you glanced back, he was gone.

Inevitable changes

'I AM SAD TO ANNOUNCE that Mister McDonald, Head of our English and Foreign Language Department, has taken a teaching role within newly established Selwyn College.' The newly installed tall, thin, grim, gravel-voiced headmaster, to whom fate had appropriately conferred the moniker Dr Craven, said it deadpan and nobody blinked. 'If it is a significant loss for us, it is a special advancement for him, since, following a twenty-year term with us, he has returned to his home town of Auckland. We extend our warm congratulations to Selwyn for securing his services, and our prayers go with him.'

'Ah, Johnny! You caught the big 'if' right?'

' "*If* it is a significant loss." Yeah.'

'Given the cloakroom caper, his career here was over. Selwyn was his escape hatch. They've no idea what kind of beast they've let into the playground.'

'Maybe he'll change his ways.'

'Or not. Cruelty runs deep.'

'I guess.'

Soapy's absence eased the anxiety, but not the perils.

'You failed School Certificate, Master Wareham.' Dr Craven's newly installed antique Persian carpet was softer than the boards in the corridor, but threadbare, nonetheless. 'We may have to hold you back a year.' Sun streamed through the window onto his back, casting you in a shadow. It was difficult to catch the expressions in his gaunt face.

'I got the passing grade, Sir—200.'

'Yes, that is both the *precise* and the *minimum* passing score, 200 out of 400. But to earn a pass you also needed to score at least *thirty* percent in two other subjects, which you did not do, and so you failed this vital *national* examination.' He tossed the pink paper onto his desk. 'You've put an unpleasant spotlight on this entire institution.' His deeply timbred voice was hypnotic. Had he missed a greater calling? 'No one in the history of this school—perhaps even of any school in the entire country—has ever done this. It is a curious achievement. What were you thinking, boy?'

That biology and geography were dead boring.

'I figured 200 would be enough, Sir.'

'Well, you clearly left something out of the equation. That you failed the examination while earning an apparent passing grade has attracted unwanted attention from the Department of Education. You have tarnished the school's reputation'—he pulled at a strand of his oily comb-over—'and placed me in a predicament. You should properly be held back a year.'

He took a deep breath and gave birth to a faint smile. 'Now, even though it is unheard of for a boy without School Certificate to pass the infinitely more stringent university entrance examinations, you might just be able to do that. A bright boy like yourself could conceivably advance to the sixth form to study for those. *Now*'—he produced the parental forefinger—'bear in mind that the school has the power to *pronounce* that a student has earned entrance to university. This is called *accreditation*. It is based upon the quality of work you do during the course of the year. And, in the normal course of events, every serious sixth-former is accredited.'

'Yes, Sir, I understand.'

'Then you'll also understand, I hope, the fate of the few who *fail* to earn accreditation.'

'Ah, yes, Sir. They sit the exam.'

'And?'

'I'm told they fail it, Sir.'

'They do indeed! So now that you fully understand the stakes, I am prepared to advance you into the sixth form on the basis of your promise to me that you will take *all* of your classes seriously, and that you will attend to *all* of your studies with due diligence. Do I have that assurance?'

Maybe. No point in hanging back a year. Anyway, so long as a subject was interesting you never doubted your ability to master it. Somehow, though, the musty rooms, the gloomy corridors, the oppressive, tweedy cane-carriers bent on inflicting education, the mindlessness of the muscular Christians, the relentless physicality of just about everything and the vacuousness of the small-town streets—all of this left you yearning to break free. Or maybe you were merely trying to survive. And maybe the best way to do that—and defend yourself against all of the above—was to disappear within an insouciant shell. But this was a new year. And the man was right. Having already failed School Certificate, he was offering you a get-out-of-jail-free card.

'Yes, Sir. Of course, Sir.'

'So be it, then. But just to make sure you're shaping up, I'll need to keep an eye on you. To that end, you must also invest one period a week in my office handling clerical duties.'

No matter. A weekly stint in this inner sanctum could be intriguing.

'Thank you, Sir.'

●

'Wilson's gone!' Ted was confused. 'He quit—who'da believed it. Who's gonna coach the first fifteen now?'

'The graveyard's full of indispensable men, chaps. The departure was inevitable. Our ambitious Latin master and rugby maven has been applying—and getting turned down—for headier jobs all over the country. His best shot, though, was to succeed Peggy as headmaster right here. He made the short list, then got the thumbs down. It was embarrassing, so he started looking outside the country and accepted the first offer he got.'

'How do you know all this?'

'Wheels within wheels. A family friend is in the loop and I thought it right to eavesdrop.'

'Where's he gone?'

'To an Aussie college as Latin master'—he grinned—'not much competition there for that job.'

'They've got a great rugby team. I love those Wallabies.'

'So he really is, uh, gone?'

'He really is.'

Was that great news? For sure, within these crazy cloisters you were now truly on your own. But you could handle that.

'Who's the new man? What's he like?'

'Time will reveal the face, the heart and the soul.'

—| |—

'Coyle's been appointed head prefect—it's a travesty!' Shell seemed more confident and adult than ever, worldlier, too, maybe.

Ted shook his head in wonderment. 'God only knows why Coke went to bat for him.'

'Petit a patribus a filio, sed et serpens.'

'Huh?'

'He seeks a son, but sires a snake.'

'What does it tell us about Coke?'

'Merely that he's a gym teacher with ambitions beyond his talent.

It's crazy, of course, but he hopes to fulfil his dreams by championing a second-rater like himself.'

'Maybe Coyle will rise to the occasion.'

'For Coyle to rise, pigs must learn to fly.'

'"*Water, water, everywhere!*"' This was a change. You'd landed, unsurprisingly, in the sixth-form B-stream, but that was just fine. The implike second-string English master, affectionately known as Hugs, loved to perform. '"*And all the boards did shrink.*"' He was easy to listen to. '"*Water, water everywhere,*"'—he paused dramatically upon his little stage—'"*nor any drop to drink.*" So lads'—he tucked a thumb into his tweed waistcoat—'there they are trapped on a cursed craft beneath a scorching sun in the middle of the doldrums—"*As idle as a painted ship, upon a painted ocean.*" That mysterious Ancient Mariner has shared quite an image with us, right, lads? They're all dying of thirst, and going nowhere.'

If the guys in the A-stream were being enlightened by a more highly credentialled fellow, who cared? This diminutive chap shared an infectious enthusiasm for words and rhymes. Perhaps your admiration for his easy, musical delivery sprang from the albatross of the stutter that hung from your neck. But no matter. A great poem could make the impediment disappear and, for a while anyway, the school, too.

Troubled lad

'YES, HE'S A TROUBLED LAD.' Craven whispered the words, but from your vantage-point outside the door you heard them, anyway. 'But like many stutterers, he's also reasonably intelligent.'

'Slothful he is not,' said Cloggs. 'Intransigent he is.'

'Intransigent?'

'And arrogant and godless.'

'Godless? I thought he was Catholic.'

'If it suits him, only. He is wilful.'

'Wilful? He mostly seems shy and quiet.'

'He reads wrongfully. And likes impious moving pictures.'

'And you're here because you have a suggestion on how to handle him?'

'Yes. Special mathematics coaching. For the examinations. Which now are nigh.'

'That could be a good idea?'

'Given his seeming intelligence, this important sixth-form year if he fails, teachers may be blamed.'

'That is true, of course.'

Intelligent—reasonably—but troubled. Who cares? Private coaching was not uncommon. Cloggs had quite a little thing going, actually. So where was the downside?

'Looking to find yourself on the big screen are you?' The theatre cashier let the half-crown lie on the granite bench. She was pert and pretty and showed a hint of soft white cleavage. Her eyes sparkled and cherry lipstick garnished her neat bow mouth. 'You wanna be Brando on a bike?' She grinned. 'Cat got your tongue?' Her teeth were even, her breath sweet.

Your new role as clerical assistant to the headmaster required you to enter officially sanctioned absences from school into a special register, then onto a blue permission card to show to any teacher whose class had to be missed. Given the boring nature of so many classes, you welcomed the opportunity to purloin a bunch of those cards and use them to assign yourself some personal time. Hence the afternoon session with The Wild One.

—|⊢—

'Xanadu! You all read it, right? So what happens? Come on, chaps, speak up.'

'A man called Kubla Khan travels to a land called Xanadu.'

'And what does he find there?'

'It's a weird place, Sir.'

'Indeed it is! Gardens, incense-bearing trees, sunny spots of greenery, caverns measureless to man, a fountain of rebounding hail, ancestral voices prophesying war.' Hugs glanced to open pages in his hand and struck his dramatic reading pose. 'This is what it was:

A savage place! as holy and enchanted
As e'er beneath a waning moon was haunted
By woman wailing for her demon-lover!

And what else does he find there, chaps?'

'A pleasure dome, Sir.'

'Yes! And not just any pleasure dome, a miracle of rare device—a *sunny* pleasure-dome with caves of *ice!* So, think about this! He not only finds a woman wailing for her demon lover, he *also* finds a sunny pleasure dome made of ice! So what might he be telling us?'

'Don't know, Sir.'

'And neither does anyone else! Coleridge dashed off this masterpiece after waking from an opium-influenced dream. Perhaps that's why he shows nature to be threatening. And perhaps the wailing woman and the sunny-icy pleasure dome are *one and the same!*' He flashed a brief grin. 'The tragedy, lads, is that while Coleridge was still working on the poem, some idiot came knocking at his front door and broke the spell. He could never get back to that enchanted kingdom. But he tried!' He set the back of his hand to his forehead and closed his eyes in mock repose. 'Oh, yes, he tried! He came back and added a last stanza. What's it all about?'

'He sees a girl singing, Sir.'

'A damsel with a dulcimer! He tells of becoming spellbound upon hearing this young maiden singing and accompanying herself on a primitive zither. He says if he could revive that fleeting moment of ecstasy he would re-enter his dream world and re-create that pleasure dome in air—but there would be a problem!

all who heard should see him there
and all would cry, Beware, Beware.
His flashing eyes his floating hair

This fellow's ecstasy would worry them so deeply, lads, that they'd have to protect themselves and look away:

Build a circle round him thrice
And close your eyes with holy dread

But they would also envy him, and know exactly why:

For he on honey dew hath fed
and drunk the milk of paradise.'

If the cracks in the asphalt really ever did open to reveal a teeming underworld it would surely be Xanadu. You'd meet the damsel with the dulcimer. Your eyes would flash, your hair would float and you'd drink the milk of paradise. If that abyss ever did yawn, you'd jump right in and never look back.

And never come back, either.

●

'Cloggs is gonna givya private coaching? Did the same for me last year. Others, too.'

'Five sessions?'

'Yeah, and *very* helpful.' He smiled. 'Just be sure to pay close attention to every maths exercise he leads you through'—he smiled—'and hold tight onto every scrap of paper.'

'So he is helpful, then?'

'You'll see.'

Brain oil

'SO LET US THEN together examine this problem.' Cloggs, smelling of kitchen soap, smiled solicitously and laid a sheet of paper on the desk. 'We just need to put a little oil into your brain.' A little oil might do it. So long as you didn't get waylaid by other distractions, you enjoyed algebra. You understood the big picture but the devil was in the details. You studied Cloggs' immaculate script. It was the same issue he'd covered in class. He sat alongside you, closely watching the pencil in your hand. 'That is good—yes! Now let us advance the battle.' He produced a somewhat trickier example of the same problem. 'Yes, again, very good.'

—|⊢—

Pock, pock—pock, pock—pock, pock. It was not match point in the College House table tennis championship, but a crucial moment, just the same. You'd drawn the illustrious Gloyn. Now in his final year, he was, as in so many years past, favoured to win the championship. He was both a stylish racquets champion and a dazzling all-round athlete. No higher compliment could be paid than Coke's selection of Gloyn to showcase his talents—and Coke's coaching prowess—in the vital first-fifteen, fly-half rugby role. But, alas, this particular game of table tennis, against the unlikely College House stutterer, before Coke himself and a jam-packed room of spectators, seemed to be going off script. You were winning by two sets to nil, and ahead handily in this potential clincher. To you, anyway, the ball also seemed to be larger than usual, and travelling more slowly than usual. You could do nothing wrong. The match would be yours. You won that point, then, mere minutes later, the match. Gloyn was no academic, but knew to offer a congratulatory hand. Coke wrapped an arm around his fallen warrior's shoulder and steered him out the door.

•

'You gotta see this—come on, Coyle's caught him!' You weren't sure you wanted to see what the sallow-skinned, sly and slippery head prefect was up to, but you stepped out the door into the darkness, anyway, and drifted to the sounds of a mêlée on the edge of the moonlit football field.

'You filthy faggot!' Coyle's voice dripped with contempt. He'd lured a hapless fellow from a home in a nearby street to the moonlit football field, then ambushed him with a half-dozen co-conspirators. The mission, apparently, was to educate the fellow, who lay trembling and trouserless within the shadowed circle of their angry feet and righteous eyes, on the morality and consequences of sexual adventures. 'Get up, up, up! Get up now! Now!' The fellow attempted to rise to his feet, but Coyle swung a jolt to the jaw that sent him back to the grass. He was maybe eighteen years old, naked from the waist down, and wearing an open-neck shirt. Until that moment, you were unaware that homosexuality might attract such violence. It seemed more a sin than a crime, more a frailty than a predilection, so why the savagery?

As the fellow lay quailing within the circle, you recalled catching sight of that same fellow on a grey day a couple of weeks earlier. A Venetian blind hid his face as he stood naked in the picture window of a bungalow just two blocks from College House. The feet were together on the inside window sill. The outstretched arms hung from the frame. You stood there for maybe a minute; the fellow never moved a muscle. It was a depressing image. Maybe he was a zealot reliving the crucifixion. Or maybe he was just plain crazy and needed help. You moved on and never bothered to mention the incident to anyone. Someone clearly did, though, and now the help had arrived.

'Get up—UP!' The fellow rolled painfully onto all fours and attempted to stand. This time Coyle swung with his boot. 'You piece of shit! Did you think that we're like you? Well, we are not! We're not like him, are we chaps? We're here to teach this piece of shit a lesson—right?' Inspired by these brave words, the buddies got into the swing of things. Boots, fists and all, in the dark shadows of night they shake-rattled-and-rolled the bleeding offender across the field. Finally, leaving him semi-conscious to tend his wounds, they turned their backs and Coyle led them laughing in a canter back across the field.

●

'How's the private coaching going?'
'Seems okay.'
'Didja hang onto the paperwork?'
'I figured my Dad had paid for it, so I might as well.'
'Exams are tomorrow. So unfurl those papers'—his lips formed a faintly ironic smile—'and study them again tonight.'
'If you say so.'

●

'Spiritual pride is another of the Devil's cunning tactics. Satan whispers that *you* know more than everyone else about the Bible, the sacraments, the catechism, about spirituality. Now, knowing things is fine, but it doesn't make you better than the ordinary Joe who's not studied theology. So don't fall for Satan's flattery. So long as our doings come from our hearts and humility, we beat him every time.'

●

'Until I am telling you to begin you must keep the sheets face down on the desk.' The room was deathly silent as he floated between the desks distributing the examination papers.

It was a moment of truth. You were confident, of course. You'd done more than enough to get a good grade. Those brain lubes might pay off, too.

'So now begin.'

You turned the papers upward. Ten problems lay in wait. How difficult might they be? You looked a little more closely. What the hell! Were these *exactly* the same problems for which your brain had been anointed? Close indeed.

You finished a perfect paper with time to spare. Cloggs was sitting at his desk atop the little stage, one eye on a book, the other on the class. As you shared a fleeting glance your relief turned to unease. Your mind raced back to the ironic smile. And the cryptic advice, *Just be sure to pay very close attention . . . and hold onto every scrap of paper.* So, now you knew what your confidant was careful not to say. He knew the game was rigged. And that you'd soon come to know it, too. You felt abused and betrayed. Everyone deserved better than this. Cloggs remained impassive and scanned the room. If he was looking for cheats, he'd need a mirror. So this was what hypocrisy looked like. Oh, what may man within him hide, though angel on the outward side.

Redemption

'I WILL NOW READ the names of the boys who have been accredited entrance to university'—he licked a dab of spittle from his thick lower lip—'and who therefore will not have to sit the upcoming national university entrance examinations.'

The room fell deathly silent.

Shell nudged you.

This was the moment.

You remembered Craven's caveat. If your name was not on the list you were done for. Some had tried, but nobody who failed to make the cut had ever sat and passed the exam. The idea was to prompt steady study work during the year and to ensure that examination anxiety did not torpedo otherwise competent students.

On any alphabetical list of names, yours was always among the last. You'd have to wait until Craven's deathly gravel voice had intoned sixty others.

●

'The Devil's sin was pride. Satan wanted to be God. Now, the opposite of pride is humility. Humble people are the most successful prayer warriors. The more you humbly pray in adoration, contrition and thanksgiving, the easier it becomes.'

'You did it, Johnny!' Shell added a happy grin to his soft nudge.

'Yeah. The pressure's off. Now what?'

'Just a month to the end of the year.'

'A month?'

'For us, yes. Only fifth-formers get to choose whether they show up for classes.'

'How come?'

'You've forgotten already? They get that time off to prepare for—and sit—the School Certificate exams.'

'The ones I failed last year?'

'Everybody knows that was a hiccup. And now, you're famous—the only university student to have failed school cert.'

'That's an honour?'

'Kind of.' He removed his glasses. 'Of course, you could always become a time-traveller.'

'A time-traveller?'

'Pretend you're a fifth-former again. Take off the whole next month.'

'How?'

'Tell Craven you feel uncomfortable going forward without having passed the School Cert exam. Say that on a matter of principle, you need to sit the exam. He'll have to give you the time off. There's no supervision, so you can do whatever you want. You'll just have to waste five half-days sitting the exams. But that'll be a piece of cake.'

'A piece of cake?'

'Sure. School Cert's just fifth-form stuff. And you've already completed sixth form. Just do it. Exitus acta probat.'

'Huh?'

'The result will validate the deed.'

'We are all servants of God, no matter how much or little we know. And remember this! Satan will *always* outwit us with his knowledge, because he truly does have a superior intellect.'

●

'Congratulations, John.' Upton Wright extended his hand. 'I was praying for your success.' His smile was benign. 'Several other Crusaders were, too.'

'You, uh, *prayed*—for *me?*'

'You seemed lost last year. Something was wrong. You'd never have failed School Certificate otherwise.'

'And the prayers, they, uh, paid off?'

'You got accredited.'

'Because you prayed?'

'We can't always see the Lord at work in our lives.'

'I guess.'

He waved his hand over the football field. 'Is it all the product of blind chance?'

'The grass?'

'The trees, the grass, the sunset, the masters who tend to our needs.'

'Coke and company?'

'He's a good man, Johnny. Christ's at work within the hearts of all our masters, through the body of the entire school, actually.'

'Maybe.'

'Look, Johnny, there are only two ways to see things. Either this is all accident or it is the result of design and plan. You might shrug your shoulders and just say that's a matter of personal opinion and let it go at that. You might, that is, except that this is a matter that will affect your whole life. It is going to determine how you think and how you live.' So, he really did sign on to that Crusader thing. 'If man is just an accident, then he has no responsibility except that which he takes upon himself. There is no law except the law of convenience and desire. There is no ultimate right or wrong and when people think and live according to that philosophy the result is chaos. But if, on the other hand, there is a plan, then there is a planner. If there is a design, there is a designer. If we find a watch in the woods, we know that a watchmaker created it. In other words, there *is* a God.

'Uh, isn't that what, uh, Shell calls a non sequitur?

'Oh, some people get confused by the maze of conflicting arguments and go round in circles. For others, the problem only gets complicated when they worry about who owns the watch. Believing in God involves a responsibility that they don't want. They don't want anybody telling them what's right or what's wrong or how to live or act.'

'Who does?'

'You don't want to listen to God who made you?'

'Isn't, uh, that, uh, begging the, uh, question?'

'Faith takes us to places that logic cannot. When you get as many people as there are in the world today living and acting as if there were no God, it's no wonder the world is in a mess. When we see the results of unbelief it doesn't seem at all far-fetched to say that the only hope for the world as a whole or for you as an individual is faith in God. Not just belief in a supreme being or a great force, but belief in a personal God who loves you enough to provide a salvation for you.'

'Doesn't, uh, wor-work for me.'

'God could cure your stutter, Johnny.' He set his hand upon your shoulder. 'He wants me to tell you that.'

'Thanks.'

Back to
the future

'A MATTER OF PRINCIPLE, you say?' You could almost hear the cogs turning in Craven's skull. Were you a wretched rascal? Probably. Or had the ministrations of the manly masters, perhaps even the prayers of concerned Crusaders, created an awakening in a saintly fellow? Unlikely.

'Quite apart from the fact that it is totally unnecessary for you to sit that examination, you do realise that if you fail, you will embarrass the school as well as yourself.' He scratched his head and gazed out the window. 'The authorities will ask how we could possibly have accredited university entrance to a boy who then ran backwards and failed School Certificate.' He turned and fixed you with his bloodhound eyes. 'It is unthinkable.'

You replied with stony silence. Why bother to engage him? He knew you were standing on the higher moral ground and that he was blocking the path of righteousness. How could he possibly deny a former sinner—who also happened to be a pitiful stutterer—the right to *redeem* a past ignominy?

Honestly, what the fuck was he thinking?

•

'Gangster movies—you like them, right? Yes? Then you're gonna love this one. *The Big Heat* is great stuff. Honest cop takes on evil forces. You could maybe pass for Glenn Ford yourself one day.'

'One day?'

'Hey, you broke the silence. Yes, one day. One day soon, maybe. I see you as more of a Glenn Ford than a Marlon Brando. Hang on, let me take a good look. Well, maybe three parts Ford and one part Brando.'

'So you really like movies?'

'Wouldn't do this job otherwise. I see everything worth seeing. Maybe one day we'll talk about the movies we've seen.'

'Really?'

'Why not?'

●

Drowsy bliss? Sounds like a great idea. Dr Van De Velde doubtless enjoys his teaching role. Somehow though, the clinical style, though helpful, can also be a little depressing.

> The accumulation or summation of excitement necessary for both the male and female orgasm, in order to reach the acme of pleasure, is achieved through a succession of stroking or thrusting movements (friction). As the phallus is rubbed and pressed against the folds and pads of the vaginal walls (especially of the anterior surface) the nerves of the male organ, and especially of its tip or glans, become so stimulated that tension is finally relieved in the sympathetic–spinal reflex discharge or ejaculation. Concurrently, the increasing and overwhelming sensory impressions received by the cerebral cortex (higher nerve centres) are felt psychically as acute pleasure. These feelings increase in force till they attain their summit in the second in which ejaculation begins. When ejaculation occurs, the pleasurable sensations continue in the form of satisfied relaxation and relief. When it ceases, the orgasm or

physical discharge is at an end. The psychic and physical sensations die away, into gratification (bien-être), a sort of drowsy bliss.

How can one think about all this? Maybe we don't need to. Maybe it all happens more naturally than the earnest doctor realises.

●

She was right about the movie. Glenn Ford was great. Icy and angry and kind of mysterious. Got drawn into a murky underworld. A touch of that might enliven this town. Too much to hope for. You looked for her on the way out but she'd flown the coop. Did she really want to talk to you? Unlikely.

●

'Ilford paper is as lovely as their film. It's English, you might study up on it.'
    'That's kind of funny.'
    'Funny?'
    'Telling me to study English.'
    'How so?'
    'I have an English exam tomorrow.'
    'Chance, Apollo, is the pseudonym of God when he does not wish to sign his work.'

Great writing

YOU WERE SITTING ALONGSIDE Shell and Ted at the long library table. September sun streamed over your shoulder, and fell upon the broadsheet pages of the *Manawatu Daily Times*. A headline, all in capitals, caught your attention.

From Sour Grapes And Twisted Vine Comes Sweet White Wine?
Splenetic Book By PN Author Who Lost The Headmastership

'Hey, look at this.' Shell tossed aside his copy of *National Geographic* and studied the sun-filled page. 'That's quite a headline. The editor must be looking to increase sales.' His eyes slipped to the opening paragraph. He whispered it aloud:

It will be surprising if Palmerston North readers of the latest novel by Palmerston North born and educated Guthrie Wilson, do not associate the chief character and hero with the author.

'Hmm—'It will be surprising *if*—kind of weaselly, don't you think, to suggest right off the bat that a work of fiction—a novel by an already acclaimed novelist, no less—is actually a work of non-fiction?'

It will be equally surprising if the same readers do not arrive at the conclusion that Mr Wilson had used his book as a vehicle to vent his spleen against the Palmerston North High School's Board of Governors for having the temerity to reject his services as rector of the boys high school.

'"It will be equally surprising"—the reviewer begs the question yet again. Very interesting. I mean we already know that before he resigned Wilson got turned down by countless other school boards, so the reviewer's logic is iffy at best . . . Ah, here's a quote from the book itself:

> I was suspected by the small right men with grey faces and stomach ulcers whom democracy so often vomits to authority over us. . . . Since in my country a school board will always contain too many conventional, timid people and they always appoint their own kind.

'Goodness—a vomit full of grey-faced men with stomach ulcers! The fictional hero's insults may be justified, but the real-life author's a bitter man, too. Just as Wilson turned the cane on us, he's tried to turn the pen on the governing boards that didn't trust him to manage their kids. Their conventional reasoning may have been all wrong, but their timidity—their intuitions, actually—were pretty good.' He tossed the paper back to you. 'I have it on the quiet that Soapy tweaked the grammar.'

'Really?'

'Yeah, and that Betty typed up the manuscript.'

'She's more than just a looker, then. It was a team effort all the way.'

'Won't matter. The review was reckless, as the paper may discover. Wilson's a bully. He might just come out looking for revenge.'

●

It didn't take long to finish *The Long Wait*. The cover was great and the story was wild. And, as promised by the red-headed goddess on the cover, you got to meet yet another nymphomaniac exhibitionist with a great body. But Mike Hammer was missing. Maybe he appears in the next book. You headed to Whitcombes.

'Do you have anything new by Mickey Spillane?'

The poncy clerk pursed his lips and shot you a look. 'His latest was *Kiss Me Deadly*, but it sold out as soon as we got it. A movie's on the way. How they'll get all that violence and sex onto the screen is anybody's guess.'

'You've nothing at all by Mickey Spillane?'

'Only *I, the Jury*—but you've read it already, yes? Yes! Well, since you're a precocious fan, there's an author interview in the latest *True Detective*. It's on the mezzanine.'

And there it was.

'You gonna buy that article, kid?' The twang was American.

'Uh, maybe.'

'Let me get it for you.' He grabbed the magazine. He was forty or so, maybe older, and wearing a white cotton tee-shirt under a denim motorcycle jacket. 'You wanna get a drink?' Crewcut, hard face, strong chin. Nice smile. He seemed okay. Not Pottsian.

'Uh, maybe.'

'I'm a writer between books. My wife wanted me to take a break. We're driving through your lovely country.' He smiled. 'It's also kind of boring. I saw what you were reading, so I thought let's talk. We're staying at the Empire. Let's go there and rest our butts.'

The 1890s ranch-style Empire Hotel complemented the denim jacket. He summoned the waiter. 'Bring us a couple milkshakes'—he nodded to you—'chocolate's good, right?' He paused. 'So, what is it with you and Mickey Spillane?'

'I loved his first book. Then I got hooked.'

'You liked it? *I, the Jury*. You were old enough to read that?'

'Sure.'

'What caught your fancy?'

'It had a great ending.'

'What about the opening? "I shook the rain from my hat and walked into the room."'

'You read it, too!'

'Listen, kid, I *wrote* that book.'

'*You're* the author?'

'I'm a writer, not an author. Authors want a place in history. I just want to keep the smoke coming out of the chimney. I dropped into that bookstore to see if my books were selling. I didn't expect to see the magazine piece'—he grinned—'nor a kid reading it.'

'I read everything. Right now I'm mostly into Shakespeare.'

'Shakespeare? Four hundred years on and still selling. If the public likes you, you're good. I don't give a hoot about reviews. I don't think he did, either. I like to read royalty checks.'

'So, what's the secret, exactly, to writing a bestseller?'

'Exactly? Well, I'll tell you. The first secret is the first page—and the last secret is the last page. They read it to get to the end, not the middle. If it's a letdown, they won't buy any more. The first page sells the book. The last page sells the next one.'

'What about sex and violence?'

'Violence outsells sex. Mike Hammer is more vigilante than detective. He never runs from a fight.'

'He dishes it out.'

'People like bad guys to get roughed up. Most people eat peanuts, not caviar. Big-shot writers never seem to get that.'

'Like Hemingway.'

'Hemingway? He's all hat and no cattle. Every summer I went down to Florida on treasure hunts, and this great restaurant had a picture of Hemingway behind the bar. The owner asks for a picture of me to put up there. One day Hemingway sees my picture and says take his down or mine down. So they took his down and he never went back!' He chuckled. 'He was a great reporter, just got carried away with all the bullfighting. I'm with the bull. If they're putting him there to kill him, I say don't stick things in him first. I used to love to watch the bison.

One day an old male died, and you know what? The others stood around him for two, maybe three days. No one could get the body out. Finally they moved aside. It was as if they decided, okay, now you can come get the body. Now what am I talking about dead bulls for?'

'Maybe you're religious?'

'Hey, kid! Something's in play! You're a believer?'

'I was baptised Catholic. It didn't work.'

'Me neither. Then a fella came to the door. I saw the light and became one of Jehovah's Witnesses.'

'You joined?'

'You don't join. You just go out and witness. You say what you saw.'

'What'd you see, exactly?'

'I saw people out of whack and a world that needed help. And I realised I could make a difference.'

'You became a believer?'

'I never say I believe—I *know*. I got gripped by something stronger than myself, something called God. I felt a transforming presence and I wanted to share it.'

'You knock on doors—all of that?'

'Some days I don't need to. Like today, maybe the person I needed to meet was sitting in a bookshop.'

'What would you say if you met him?'

'I'd invite him to be part of a peaceful, loving society that's being created right here on earth right now.'

'How're you gonna do that, exactly?'

'We're ridding greed and corruption and building a brotherhood that'll enjoy perfect health in an earth-wide Paradise.'

'What'll happen to the bad guys?'

'They'll be removed.'

'To hell?'

'There's no hell. When someone dies nothing remains. But good people—authentic witnesses—remain in God's memory. One day they'll be brought back to life. The unworthy will remain dead.'

'So there really is a second coming?'

'The Greek word was *presence*, not *coming*. I believe in the presence of Christ like you believe in Shakespeare. You can feel how he shapes your language, right?'

'Maybe.'

'Religion's turned everything inside out. Someone says how'd you like to live forever? You say, "Oh boy. I'd love that. What've I gotta do?" And Jesus says, "You just gotta know God—the one and only true God." It's not the end of the world we witness. It's the coming of the peace of God, the end of the system of things as they are. It's all about taking in knowledge.'

'Becoming enlightened?'

'I get excited about this. If you don't say stop I'll keep talking. But this is why people think I'm nutty. "Don't people turn you down?" they ask. But they turn God down, not me. That's why the world's the way it is.' He paused. 'Am I saying too much?'

'I like what you're saying. And I'm thinking that our meeting, having read your book and all, might be some kind of, uh, destiny. If I'm confused, I guess the book confused me. I mean all that sex and violence—and now suddenly I find that the author—I mean the writer—is a good guy trying to save the world.'

'*I'm* not saving the world, kid. I'm just witnessing what went down. I don't smoke and I don't drink. Okay, I have a beer once in a while, but that's okay because the Bible only condemns drunkenness. Some say I'm bad because of what I wrote. But we all gotta eat. I needed money to make a down-payment on a home, so I wrote *I, the Jury* in nine days. Nine days! It made me the money, then it made me famous—for a good reason. God was on my side because I was on the side of the good guys. Always. Mike Hammer only roughed up bad people. Yeah, he killed them, too. Rotten people, evil people. God liked the book and called me to become a witness. He wanted more of the same. Someone comes up and says, "How could Mike Hammer have possibly shot that naked broad right in the belly button?" I say she was bad—*really* bad. Mike never goes after ordinary gangsters. He goes after Commies—evil people stealing atomic secrets and adulterating movies with red propaganda. I was happy to have Mike Hammer use a Chicago typewriter—a submachine gun, in case you didn't know— to tap out one-way tickets to heaven for Commie heavies and fellow-travellers. That was another book. You might like to read it.'

●

'*Sweet White Wine?*' The librarian cocked an eye and pursed her lips. 'Lot's of interest in that. It's got quite a little brouhaha going, actually. The loan copies are all out, but you can read this one—so long as you stay here, of course.'

You flipped to the inside flap. *Guthrie Wilson has been hailed as 'one of New Zealand's most important writers since Katherine Mansfield.'* Maybe so. You opened to a middle page and your eye came to rest on a sentence. *It's a refreshing experience to sit down and examine with fairness a human structure with whom one has attained some degree of intimacy.* Human structure? Sit down and examine with fairness? What about some simpler nouns and verbs? You flipped to another page. *I accompanied him on his voyages to the homes of the many girls he had left behind him. There was a staggering number of them.* Yikes— singular and plural ambiguity. Should've recast the sentence. Give it one last shot. *We hugged and kissed in the way that men and women have behaved since this earth regurgitated them from the caverns of its flaming intestines.* The earth's flaming intestines? Really! Time was short. No point reading more.

You returned the book to the counter.

'Too adult for you?'

'Maybe. Do you, uh, have any, uh, Mickey Spillane?'

Afternoon delights

'WAGGING SCHOOL AGAIN, are we?' She tossed back the change. 'Well, serves you right.' Her grin morphed into a smile. 'This isn't Wild One or Big Heat. It's something to talk about, but a box office dud, too. You'll have the place to yourself.'

The place to yourself? Oh, Johnny, the thoughts that raced through your head. Would you care to join me? We could sit in the back row and share the darkness. We could touch. We could savour the thrill of the rising credits. I could run my fingers through that shiny onyx hair. I could taste those cherry lips. We could depart this world and enter another.

'We could talk about it later?'

'Sure, why not?'

The local denizens must be zombies. Laurence Olivier's Hamlet was being touted as hot, sexier even than Brando in his toga.

You settled back into your seat.

This is the tragedy of a man who could not make up his mind

Oh, no! That dumb-down line was never penned by the Bard. Who injected it? And is Olivier's voice too plummy?

Tis not alone my inky cloak, good mother . . .

Happily, with his solemn suit and silver-blond hair, he looks the part.

I have that within that passeth show . . .

Maybe yes and maybe no. The moody monochrome photography is terrific. So is the lighting.

And here's something . . .

I have of late—but wherefore I know not—lost all my mirth . . . it goes so heavily with my disposition that this goodly frame, the earth, seems to me a sterile promontory

Right—the entire school's a depressing tomb.

This most excellent canopy, the air, look you, this brave o'erhanging firmament, this majestical roof fretted with golden fire—why, it appears no other thing to me than a foul and pestilent congregation of vapours.

Drab buildings, gloomy corridors, soulless surroundings—even on the brightest days.

He's climbing the shadowy stairs to spooky music:

I will speak daggers to her, but use none

Daggers. Wagging school are you?

The queen's in her bedroom in a low-cut gown.

He's grabbed her by the arm:

Come, come, and sit you down

He's tossed her onto the bed.

You shall not budge

A dud? No—not at all. This, Veronica, is hot stuff. If only you were here sitting alongside me, you'd know.

You go not till I set you up a glass, where you may see the inmost part of you.

Kill that old fool behind the curtain first.

How now! A rat? Dead, for a ducat, dead! Thou wretched, rash, intruding fool, farewell!

There goes Polonius.

And here's Hamlet back on the bed with her again.

You cannot call it love; for at your age, the hey-day in the blood is tame, it's humble, and waits upon the judgement.

The burning pubis burns itself out? Maybe that happened to Coke. Cat got your tongue? Perhaps she was burning for you to speak.

And so you live in the rank sweat of an enseamed bed, stew'd in corruption—

He has her by the wrists, her face inches from his.

Serves you right. Was she teasing or tempting?

He tosses her back on the bed. She's plump but gorgeous. The outline of her nipples is plain to see:

honeying and making love over the nasty corpse

The gown is off her shoulders.

She's lovely, actually.

His father's ghost—the coinage of Hamlet's brain?—comes then goes. What's Hamlet thinking?

Good night: but go not to mine uncle's bed.
And when you are desirous to be bless'd,
I'll blessing beg of you.

He kisses her—and rather passionately, too.

If only you'd done the same. What was it about that girl? It was something. The winsome smile perhaps? She was saying something, surely.

Help, angels! Make assay!

The King—that sinning uncle—is soliloquising.

Bow, stubborn knees; and, heart with strings of steel
Be soft as sinews of the newborn babe!

So, Claudius is down on his knees praying—or so it seems to Hamlet, peeking from the corridor.

Now might I do it pat, now he is praying.

Kill him, Hamlet. The moment is right. Kill him.

And so he goes to heaven?

Please, there's no such place:

A villain kills my father; and for that, I, his sole son, do this same villain send to heaven?

Yes, dispatch him now. Move him along. Assume the crown yourself.

O, this is hire and salary, not revenge.

Yes it *is* revenge. Get it while you can.

No! trip him, when his soul may be as damn'd and black as hell, whereto it goes.

—| |—

She was still there, that pretty bird in the silver cage.

'You liked it then?'

'Uh, yes.'

'So what was it all about?'

It was about you and me. I was Hamlet. You were the fair Ophelia. You loved me and I loved you. We drove each other crazy. Your father split us up and I killed him. Well, not deliberately. I mistook him for my uncle who murdered my father so he could inherit the crown and make off with my mother. I killed my uncle, too. Took me forever to do it, but in the end I gave him what he deserved. Not before he poisoned my mother, though. Well, everybody died in the end, including me. But that's life, right? There's a special providence in the fall of a sparrow. It comes to us all. Right now, though, you're so lovely and full of life that the cat's got my tongue.

'A man who couldn't make up his mind?'

'Oh, God, no!' She grinned. 'Olivier concocted that line.' So, she's a movie buff. 'And he picked a girl young enough to be his daughter to play the part of his mother—what do you think of that?'

'The Queen was younger than Hamlet?'

'In real life Olivier was forty and Eileen Herlie was twenty-nine—that's a big age difference, right?'

'I, uh, didn't notice. She looked okay to me.'

'She's a great actress. And who cares, anyway? I mean, I'm older than you and we're having a nice conversation.' She glanced at the roman numerals on the clock behind her. 'Next screening's not till tonight. Wanna share a lemonade and talk about the movie?'

'Uh, yes. Where?'

'Around the corner.'

Around the corner? Might she lead you to the luminous Xanadu you stopped to admire after slipping the prison walls and making your way into town? Every other dwelling in the wide, dead-boring street was an unremarkable box. Broken-souled gates hung from tired hinges. Fading curtains cloaked the absence of life. But not so here at this house. The paint and trim were complementary pastels. A shaft of sun lit a line of pink bougainvillea woven into the picket fence. You heard a rustling and noticed a rear garden pergola within which, oblivious to the world, a white-haired couple were quietly trimming a firmament of flowering vines. You stood there for a full minute, maybe even longer. That otherworldly couple noticed neither you nor the dreary, barren streets beyond their sunny bubble. Like you, they were lost. Unlike you, they were lost in each other, consumed in the creation of a home. Maybe one day you'd meet a damsel with a dulcimer and create your own Xanadu. Maybe you already had.

Her perfume was lovely and her shoulder bounced against yours. You turned off the main road onto a gravel street. The stones crackled beneath your feet. In mere minutes you arrived at a tall, wooden, creosote-painted gate. She raised the latch, and you stepped onto a soft, leafy, oak-lined driveway, at the end of which a modest, white, wooden bungalow nestled within a cluster of trees. A faint breeze hit your cheek. She brushed away a flutter of falling leaves.

Tinfoil,
twinkle, glitter, shine,
crystal edging
—whose design?

'We have the house to ourselves for the rest of the day—just like the movie. This is my room.' A picture window overlooked a tiny lawn partly shaded by a huge oak. The autumn sun peered through the thinning leaves.

Open hand
with golden dancers
granulated, falling answers

A fluffy white eiderdown covered the queen-sized bed, and reflected soft light from the bed lamp. She waved her hand over the walls. 'Like the decor?'

'Movie posters are great.'

'This is my favourite.'

'*The Reckless Moment?*'

'Yeah, it's my favourite poster. I didn't see the movie but James Mason's so suave. And whattabout this? *On the Waterfront*—whatta movie, right? And, hey, does this guy remind you of anybody?'

'James Dean? He's new.'

'Yeah. Whatta doll!' She smiled. 'Looks like you.'

'Me?'

'Yeah. Just need jeans and a tee shirt. I'm gonna call you Jimmy, anyway.' She smiled. 'Call me Veronica.'

'Veronica Lake?'

'Maybe.' She perched on the side of the bed. 'Wanna talk about Hamlet?' She kicked off her black pumps and lay back. 'Or rebels without causes?'

You set your knees into the soft eiderdown at the foot of the bed and leaned forward. She wore a green frock with subtle leaf patterns. It was white-buttoned, top to bottom. The top four were undone. You were Hamlet, she was the Queen.

'Come here. We'll talk about the movie.'

The bed was soft. A circle of cherubs adorned the centre of the plaster ceiling. Others chirped in the oak beyond the window. Dead silence, otherwise.

'I figure you can help. I know about Frank Capra and David Lean, but not much about William Shakespeare. So, what'd you think of the movie?'

'I'm still thinking.'

'What about the lighting—and the photography?'

'I liked it.'

'Liked it? Listen Jimmy, critics complain that Olivier butchered the script, but who cares? The lighting and photography saved everything. That deep-focus lens created a mix of confusion and cool. Will you ever forget those ghastly, barren, windy surroundings?' God, she was lovely. 'It fixed the forlorn characters in the frame and chased them all over Elsinore. That dead-calm camera was creepy. You felt like a Peeping Tom but you never quite knew why. Something—like a pitiless monster in a horror flick—was stalking these people. It stayed out of sight, but watched them from awesome heights and distances.' Perhaps, if she would unbutton the rest of that frock you could touch the source of her enchanting susceptibility. 'We watch the futile acts of forsaken humans through the cold, unblinking eyes of God.'

'You really do know movie making.'

She turned her face to yours. 'I'm not just a canary in a cage, Jimmy.' Her soft fingers stroked your cheek. 'What'd you make of the characters, then—really?'

She was testing you. Better have something to say. 'I'm still thinking about it . . . but maybe even from the beginning, Hamlet seems to be thinking about death.'

'Yes, the performance picks up speed as the story rushes to its tragic climax.'

'Hamlet's driven by a death wish?'

'Right, Jimmy, driven by the terrifying force of an unhappy desire to enter the undiscovered country—'

'—from whose bourn no traveller returns?'

'Right. And in this picture the melancholy prince's thrusting, aggressive wit'—she pressed her hand under your trouser leg—'and in the fatal last-act duel'—she smiled warmly, delighted apparently to find you aroused—'his feverishly exuberant swordplay have an unsettling erotic charge.' She unbuttoned her dress. Her stomach was milky, her bra white, her nipples inflamed. 'Come on Jimmy,' she whispered. She grasped your member, then encircled you with her full, warm lips. Oh, that tongue. Oh, those fingers. Oh, yes, there, sure, there, there . . .

'That was quick, Jimmy—do you have another?' She paused. 'Well, no need to ask. I'll take that as yes.'

She was a flower to the touch. She was warm and she was sweet. You cupped her breasts. 'To the hilt, Jimmy . . . to the hilt . . . to the hilt . . .' Her nails clawed your back. Her tongue silenced all your anxieties . . .

Pock—pock, pock—pock, pock—pock. It was championship point. Pock—pock. You were lost in the game. Pock—pock. And in the thrill of the moment. No need to hurry. Pock—pock. Take it easy. Pock—pock. Relax. Pock—pock. Wait for the winning shot. Pock—pock. And here it comes. Now. Yes, yes. A win, a palpable win.

'So then, Jimmy, you see, don't you, that the consummation that Hamlet wished for, death itself, will come soon enough, and then, for sure, the rest truly will be silence.'

Autumn leaves
the wind bereaves
the teardrops
of the rustling trees

'I think I get it.'

'I hope so, Jimmy. Defiance is the passageway to fun. It's all about breaking rules, seizing the moment and creating what we need.'

' "Take the cash and let the credit go"?'

'You bet. Enjoy our consummations right here and right now. There's only one showing, you know.'

●

'Fornication is a trap that the Devil springs when you feel alone and unloved. He gulls you with a bait of seeming goodness inside a snare of darkness. The jaws close the moment you yield. So spot and shun all such tempters. Remember, you feel alive and carefree in their presence, but depressed and guilty in their absence. Satan gives you sex to convince you that *you* have the secret of life, and that *we*—God's servants—are simpletons. But one day, the music will stop and you'll go to hell.'

●

Craven cleared the gravel from his throat. 'It seems we worried needlessly, Master Wareham.' The words were fine but the tone conveyed confusion 'It was a principled thing to do'—he pulled on his lower lip, doubting his own words—'courageous too, uh, perhaps.'

Yes, indeed. You aced the School Cert exam. Despite the dire doubts and fulsome forebodings, despite the fact that your mind was never in the game, despite the fact that you were mostly at the movies. But Craven was right. A principle was involved. The Pleasure Principle.

‘He's too *young*, Jack.' The Cigarilloed One shot a blast of smoke into the air, then licked the film on her upper plate of teeth. She was clearly miffed, but he pretended not to notice.

‘He's passed all his exams and he'll be a seventeen-year-old upper-sixth former in a couple of months, so it's high time he learned to drive.' He gave you a fond glance. ‘And after you've taken some lessons and passed the driving test, I'll show you how to drive the Jag.'

‘Not the *Jag!* ' She coughed and swallowed. ‘He's way too young for that, Jack.' Her fingers tightened on the yellow stem holder. ‘It's a not a toy for a boy.'

Not at all. It was a trophy for a man. But she was missing the father-and-son thing. He was passing the torch. Or the bow and arrow. Something like that.

Blazing Glory

YOU STOOD BY the College House gate and scanned the road. It was noon and a sunny day, the last of the school year. The day boys had already fled. College House inmates had to wait for their clothes and effects to be removed from the building. Parents were arriving to help load the bundles into family cars. After that, and before takeoff, Coke and Betty would host a farewell luncheon within the red-flowered, thick-scented hibiscus trees that lined the patch of grass at the house master's front door.

'Delighted to meet you, Missus Colquhoun.' The cigarillo was missing from the corner of the Loved One's mouth. She was wearing a new tailored suit and clearly on her best behaviour.

'Call me Betty, please.' In that summery yellow dress, Betty seemed quite vibrant. She was slender and supple, sexy even. A necklace of white baubles matched her low-heel shoes.

'Ah, Jack!' Resplendent in his silver-ferned New Zealand Cricket Club blazer, and beaming as if they were old friends, Coke reached out his hand.

'A pleasure to be here, Ian.'

Coke glanced to Jack's blazer and his eyes lingered momentarily over the gold monogram that precisely noted the five years the owner of same had represented the illustrious Wellington team. It was one of those moments a local boy would never forget. And for good reason. The annals of cricket record that the only time Coke played for New Zealand, he was dismissed on the first ball in both innings, and that the team itself made history by getting the lowest ever number of runs—so you wondered, since silver lettering noted the year of the debacle, that Coke wore his cricket blazer at all. In your mind anyway, Jack's cloak recorded an infinitely more notable achievement: the years he represented Wellington. Let's not forget, either, that the only reason he wore the blazer was because, as a Father's Day present, you had secretly purchased and presented him with the gold monogram. It was another father-and-son thing, though perhaps more son than father. He only ever wore the blazer to school events. Maybe to wear it was to accept he'd come up one step short of taking the field for the almighty All Blacks. Any red-blooded Kiwi contender who so faltered was merely an also-ran.

An air of relief suffused the shady setting. The year had ended and nothing terrible had happened. Parents smiled at each other, oblivious to the knowing glances exchanged by their sons; they had survived and their secrets were safe. Ham and cucumber sandwiches were partaken. Lipton's tea washed down scones, strawberry jam and cream. Coke beamed like a winning general. Betty even shot you the warmest of smiles.

'Such a lovely upper-class party, Jack.' Her cigarilloed face appeared in the mirror. 'He really is a lucky boy.'

'It's a great school, with a proud history.'

'What're we gonna do with him for the next couple of months, though?'

Riding
the tiger

THE DRIVER'S DOOR of the Jag closed with a reassuring click, as if locking you into a fighter jet. The cabin seemed as robust as a bank safe. The soft, luxurious grey leather smelled like money. The gleaming walnut dashboard showcased a bevy of impressive instrumentation.

Jack slipped into the passenger seat and handed you the ignition key. 'They call it the poor man's Rolls-Royce,' he said, 'but the Jag's got style the Rolls will never have. Grace, Space and Pace—that's what the brochure says.' He smiled, lost in his head. His face was gentle in such moments. Perhaps his private thoughts were more comforting than the Cigarilloed One's flattery.

Learning to drive the instructor's little Austin had been a snip. Handling the Jag might not be so easy. 'Let's take it into town, Johnny.' You glanced to the ornamental glass-encased jaguar head in the middle of the steering wheel, then inserted the key and hit the ignition. The engine purred. He watched as you depressed the clutch and moved the gear-stick forward. Now, ever so slowly, you released the pedal and the big beast rolled forward. The car was heavy and so was the wheel. But no matter. Best not let him see you sweat. He was more nervous than you, actually. His feet pressed non-existent passenger-side pedals. His hands poked at the air. But as your confidence grew and your skill became apparent, he gradually relaxed. Finally, as you glided the shimmering chariot into the centre of the town, he was beaming and gazing out the window, perhaps hoping to spot a friend to validate the moment. You brought the car to rest outside his office. 'Well done, Johnny,' he said. He glanced at his watch and cracked the door. 'I've got work to do.' He smiled. 'You can take it back home solo.'

You decided to take the scenic route around the bays. You eased quietly out of town. The road was windy but traffic was light. No doubt about it, the Jag had real power. Just to test it a little, you very briefly pushed the accelerator to the floor. The seat grasped you like a prize in a demon's paw. It was intoxicating.

●

'He came in a Jag!' The thick-set, pimpled bodgie boy stared into your eyes. 'Rich kid, right?'

Whatever were you doing here? Why agree to attend a social evening—a teenage dance, no less—arranged by the Saint Vincent de Paul Society? It was a deleted scene from *West Side Story*. The band was tuneless, the overhead fluorescent lights were intrusive, the kids were a mix of haplessness and menace.

If you'd been secretly hoping to meet another Veronica you were disappointed.

'Take us for a joy ride then.'

So now the movie was *Rebel Without a Cause*. A game of chicken lay ahead. You could play Jimmy Dean for Veronica, but she wasn't here tonight, and nothing good was about to happen.

'Gotta, uh, leave.'

'He's gotta, uh, *leave*. He's gotta, uh, get home to bed.' He gathered a bunch of friends and they followed you through the rain to the car. 'I wasn't kidding, see!' He waved his dirty fingernails at the glistening car. 'It really is a Jag! A big Mark Seven, too. Come on, let's take it for a spin.' He tried to grab the key from your hand. No choice was involved. You grabbed his wrist, jerked him forward, slipped your leg behind both of his and heaved him backwards. 'I'm bleeding,' he wailed as he lay on the wet asphalt, pressing a bloody hand to the back of his head. 'I think he broke my arm, too.'

A joy ride with those guys, forget it. A spin on your own was another matter. You carefully glided the vehicle through the city lights, then turned onto the main highway and headed to the beach. You pressed the accelerator and the power surge was exhilarating. Releasing that power was exciting, too. The vehicle was quite amazing, such control, even on a wet road.

As you pulled to rest, the grimy foreshore gravel cracked beneath tyres. Did the first settlers really land on this desolate, windswept beach? You watched the droplets chase each other down the windscreen. Behind them the far-off lights shimmered. Wellington was a city. Small but civilised. If you were looking for trouble you could find it. After-hours booze, even pimps, prostitutes and thugs. That was the story, anyway. Did you really break that little thug's arm? Unlikely. Maybe his head bled a little. You'd not intended that to happen. Or anything for that matter. Chance. Is life a game of chance? Can we control things? For sure, a Jag responds to the driver. Instantly, too. But a car is just a thing. People, some anyway, have minds. And imaginations. We mightn't always know what, where or who they are, but there are things we need to do, places we need to go to, people we need to meet. For sure, you met none of them tonight. Or maybe you did? Maybe you were fated to slay a dragon and dodge a game of chicken? Maybe that's what happened. Who cares? Nobody. Only you. And do you care? Not really. The window had fogged up. You stroked the condensation with your finger:

Passing through.
Where to go?
What to do?

You wiped the words away. It was time to head home. Home? An awesome Xanadu with caves of ice? What about a sunny garden and a damsel with a dulcimer?

The tyres squealed. You checked the speedo. Eighty-something. Jack wound it up to a hundred one day. 'Oh, Jack,' she'd giggled, 'You're such a daredevil!' He smiled, one eye on the road and one eye on the speedo. The goal had been achieved. He eased off and relaxed. 'Oh, *Jack*'—she reached out and stroked his hand—'you took it to *more* than a hundred miles an hour!' Was she still belching that rancid smoke inside your head? No—the tyres had taken to squealing again. It all happened quickly. You saw the concrete and steel bridge coming. And then you didn't. And then you saw it again. And then you didn't. You saw, as in a kaleidoscope, the city lights. And then you didn't. And then you did. Then everything went dead still.

Part Three
Awakenings

The bright side

JACK ALWAYS LOOKED on the bright side. He stood at the College House gates, slowly released you from a farewell hug and cast an admiring eye over the gleaming Jag. 'I prefer the new black and green two-tone to the old metallic blue,' he said. 'It looks just like the latest model.'

Incredibly, the car had been salvageable. The chassis got straightened, the rear panelling replaced, and a top-shop paint job applied. 'These new Jag colours are classier than the old ones.'

The Loved One hadn't made the trek. She was still miffed about the accident. He didn't seem to care. 'It's only a car,' he had said, surveying the midnight scene, catching the roar and the smell of passing trucks as he eyed the forlorn wreck. He smiled warmly. 'You're alive and well—it's a miracle.'

Maybe some weird divinity had indeed intervened. The out-of-control Jag had spun through the air and rammed full force into that concrete and steel bridge. Fortunately, it sailed in backwards, otherwise you'd be dead. The force tore the driver's seat from the floor. It carried the stall up and backwards and landed, with you still sitting in it, on the wide rear couch. You'd been triply insulated: by the lush driver's seat, by the bolts that slowed the ejection of the seat from the floor and by the back couch cushioning. Totally unscathed, and as if in a dream, you casually opened the back passenger door and stepped away from the car. In that moment, however, the world reappeared. You awoke standing in the middle of the slimy highway. Screeching cars swerved to avoid you. Life is more dangerous than death.

●

'Upper sixth form—who needs it?! I mean, we can go to university right now, so why don't we?'

'Ah, Johnny, it's about becoming a gentleman.'

'How will this happen, exactly?'

'Our masters will apply a final polish and instil a sense of noblesse oblige. After that, it's acta non verba.'

'Action not words?'

'Correct.'

'So how does this play out?'

'The Philistines have left, so our ranks are reduced to one class of thirty comrades. We have a full year during which we shall mature and strike the happiest of balances. With fuller and greater strength than ever, we will excel in manly sports even as we pursue wisdom with gentleness and purity.'

'There'll be no exams?'

'Only scholarship exams.'

'I thought university education was free.'

'Almost, but not quite. If you pass the exams you'll get a small, first year-stipend.'

'And if you fail?'

'Ignominy will forever trail you.'

Perhaps your greatest upper sixth form achievement was to have been the only boy in the class passed over to become a school prefect. You didn't care. You understood. But the way ahead looked dull indeed. And would've been, if you'd not made the most of things. But you did, and mostly good things happened. At least until the grim reaper came calling. He's a charming and persuasive fellow, no doubt about it.

Carpe diem

CYST, THE NEW BIOLOGY MASTER, was in full flight in front of the class when he spied the book in your bag. He stepped forward, grabbed it and studied the cover.

'*Rosicrucian Mysteries*!' His lips held the sneer as he cynically thumbed the pages. 'Really boy! Whatever are you thinking?' He hoisted the book aloft. 'This quackery emanates from Oceanside, California. It's a place bursting with weird religions. Whatever they pretend to be, they're not Christians. I should confiscate this book right now. Where did you get it?'

'Uh, public, uh, library, Sir.'

'I see,' he said, momentarily taken aback. 'And I hear you, too, Master Wareham. You're a troubled lad. I shall take no further action.' He tossed the book back onto your desk. 'But I shall expect you to forgo the study of crazy cults and apply yourself instead to biology—which I'm reliably told is your weakest subject.'

Really?

•

'Is Wilson gonna win or lose?' Ted held the paper aloft and we gathered around him.

'Conventional wisdom says nobody wins a libel case, but I'm not so sure.' Shell was into the drama of the whole thing. 'The town's agog, the newspapers are getting rich and Wilson's getting all the attention he ever dreamed of—well, almost. He just needs the Catholics to ban the book and he'll be off to the races.'

'Does he have a strategy for winning?'

'He'll say it's a novel and they'll have to prove that it's not. They'll slander him along the way, of course. They'll say that *he*—the author—truly was the hero of the tale and therefore a bad fellow. Here, see, they're calling him "a tremendously conceited, fatuous, sanctimonious ass, with a nasty streak of obscenity in his makeup".'

'Is obscenity illegal?'

'Depends on the quality of the writing.'

'What about this, then: "Jean had a body to ponder about fairly solemnly, but you knew from one glance into the unturgid depths of her steady eyes, that it had no significance to her."'

'Tells nothing about the character of the narrator, but much about Wilson. He's often guilty of rotten writing. It's hard to tell what he's trying to say.'

'Is this less murky? "She was a dear girl, a reliable competent girl who had social presence and maturity and no fanny at all. That is exactly what the best of parents would wish upon their sons."'

'Yeah, I read it earlier. Not to be picky but it might've been clearer if he'd said, "who had social presence and maturity, *but* no fanny at all".' He smiled, patiently. 'The point, however, is that neither of these clumsy extracts proves that Wilson was a bad fellow out for revenge against our sacred school.'

'And was he?'

'Morally? Yes. He was guilty of using his novel to settle scores. But not just with this reviewer. He wanted to make an even broader statement. Bear in mind that he wanted to be a famous international writer but wound up a lowly schoolteacher in a rural town. He's angry with all the people who turned him down—not just publishers and school boards, anyone who seemed to get in the way of his Hemingway dreams, including the hapless students he was paid to teach.'

'So he's gonna lose?'

'I doubt it. He's got a good lawyer and a sound legal argument: it was *fiction*—end of story.'

•

'We've got to push ourselves, Apollo. We've got to capture pictures nobody else could take. We have to hone our techniques, gather our wits and probe deeply. Cartier-Bresson used just one Leica camera, one lens, one shutter speed, one film and no flash. We all have access to private worlds and special people. Whenever you see something familiar in your viewfinder then do something to shake it up. Small things make big differences. But the biggest secret is to get out the camera and take the photo! And you know why? Because the common ingredient of great photographs is synchronicity.'

'Synchronicity?'

'You've heard of Carl Jung, yes? He realised there are no accidents, so he invented synchronicity.'

'No accidents at all?'

'Synchronicity is a meaningful coincidence.'

'But what coincides?'

'Our secret inner lives coincide with the outside world. Synchronicity explains our weird feelings of being connected with places and people—and photographs.'

'Like déjà vu?'

'Kind of. That eerie appropriateness of moments of synchronicity, the whispered voice, the hidden presence, when we think we're alone. But what looks like mere chance springs from a deep source of destiny. Synchronicities are signposts. They kindle a light and show us where to look. They signpost hidden links between us and the larger world. They express themselves through chance meetings, dreams and supernatural episodes.'

'Supernatural?'

'The universe is a theatre of mirrors. It's a set of hieroglyphs. Everything's a sign. Everything harbours and manifests mystery. A photo is a secret about a secret, and mysterious coincidences make us rethink the mystery that surrounds our lives. The more it tells, the less you know. Photos offer insights that help us grow—spiritually as well as psychologically. They show how our lives have meaning.'

'I'm definitely gonna look for signs.'

'If it were that easy everyone would be doing it. But we're like a flea on an iron bull. Soon enough, we stop trying to penetrate the impenetrable. We have to let the fickle tide of fate carry us. The eye must learn to listen before it looks. We must trust our intuitions. Logic should be a servant, not a master. When we move with the rhythms that flow through our lives we open ourselves to the wellsprings of life. We encounter more and more synchronicities, and then one day we experience the miraculous.'

'Really?'

'So I'm told.'

●

'Am I right in saying, Sir'—you were probably alone in sensing Shell's mocking tone—'that to captain a representative rugby team is a high calling?'

'The call to lead a rugby team is a serious matter, boy. It is a *very* high calling. That was especially true when I played for Wellington.'

'What, uh, years, Sir?'

'Several years, Master Wareham—several.'

He was shy to admit what Jack had already confided. 'Coke only played for Wellington when the real men were overseas fighting the Nazis.'

'My Dad played from, uh, 1934 to, uh, 1938.'

'Yes, I remember—the years are on the pocket-crest of that Wellington blazer he always wears so proudly.' He shared a smile with

Coyle and Runting. 'But did he play for the A-team or the B-team?'

'Only, uh, A-teamers get the, uh, blazer, Sir.'

'I seem to remember him playing mostly for the B-team, but perhaps he played in enough minor matchups to qualify. But no matter, boy. What matters is that he took the field.'

'It's not a game for sissies, Sir!'

'Right, Runting. It is a test of intellect and courage.'

'Brains and guts, Sir.'

'Well spoken, Coyle. You're an intelligent lad, and a fighter, too. That's why I made you flanker. Your role is to swoop down on the opposition, force them to fumble, get the ruck going and make sure the rake of the ball brings it back to us.'

'I do it like you taught me, Sir. Knocked the opposition right out of the game the other day.'

'It was a vigorous tackle. They were slow to recover.'

'One pansy just quit!'

'Ferocity is, uh, fine, Sir?'

'Rugby's a contact sport, Master Wareham. Things happen in the heat of battle.'

'My father—'

'Your father played out on the wing, so he seldom saw the intensity of the forward battle for the ball.'

'No guts, sir?'

'No guts, Runting? Who?'

'The pansy who quit the field, Sir.'

Coke mulled the remark. 'The aim is to transform pansies into mighty oaks.' He smiled. 'Ah yes, indeed, boys—mighty oaks. But for that to happen, we have to stay on the field. We have to persevere.'

'When the going gets tough, Sir—'

'Right boy'—he clenched and pumped his fist—'the tough get going.'

Toast

NO MID-MORNING MOVIE SCREENING.
It's a Monday, that's why. The town's almost closed down. It may be
boring but it beats sitting in a gloomy history class. Who gives a damn
about the lineage of British leeches? Those so-called aristocrats only
studied maps so they could change all the colours to pink. Oh, God,
those boring maps. How does anyone memorise a map? Or draw a
map? And they'd be calling for your homework. Best to be absent.
Officially absent. No problem for the trusted record-keeper—you—to
assign another leave of absence in the register.

But now that you're out of the dungeons and on the loose, what
to do, exactly? You're a little conspicuous wandering around at this
hour. You've no money, either, right? But what's this? A bookstore.
Very nice. Elegant stationery, too. And there's the proprietor back
there playing with the cash register. You owe Von a letter. Here's a
lovely little package. A writing pad with matching envelopes she'd love
to open. You didn't intend to stuff it under your grey school jersey. It
just happened.

'Hey you!' The unhealthy blast of nicotine and halitosis belonged to
the fat, bald, fiftyish proprietor. He'd crept up front and was blocking
the door while advancing in your direction. 'What's that up your
jumper, boy?' What to say? 'Speak up, boy!' You extracted the spoils
and offered them up. As he snatched the package you put your legs
into gear and dashed past him. 'I got a good look at you, boy!' Maybe

so and maybe not, right now he could only see your heels. 'And I know the headmaster,' he shouted, 'so you're toast!'

The devil came a-knocking
        at your door
and called your name.
You cracked the frame
        and whispered,
          jaw to jaw
Johnny's gone,
          this ain't his home
          no more.

●

'Didja hear what happened?' Ted was excited. You divined what was coming next. 'One of our guys got caught shoplifting.'

'Got *caught*? Wow! Whatta they gonna do with him?'

'Tried to steal stuff then did a runner.'

'So they didn't *catch* him, then?'

'Seems they will. All happened this morning and there's gonna be a lineup tomorrow. The culprit's gonna get whacked. No mercy will be shown. Then he's gonna get expelled, I bet.'

'A lineup? Who's gonna be in it?'

'Everyone with an absent pass. The names are all in the registry book.'

'Yes, of course. I wrote them up myself. You're on the list, right?'

'Yeah, I hadda go to town and buy cricket boots.'

'I remember. And you know what? *I'm* on the list, too!'

'*You're* on it? But it wasn't you, right?'

'Me? You must be joking.'

'Whoever it was knows who it was! And he'll be toast tomorrow, whoever it was.' Toast.

What to do? You'd have to show up. How then to escape detection? How might you confuse the blazing eyes within the angry, smelly face?

You glanced at your watch.

'You got here just in time, laddy'—the barber sighed—'I was about to close up.'

Samson had long hair. So did you. Didn't always go down well. Not in these backwoods, anyway. Folks said it made you look like a bodgie. Too bad for them. It looked just fine. Used to, anyway. Right now the mirror says it's time for a change. 'A crewcut, please.'

'A crewcut!' He tossed the apron over your shoulders. You shared a mirror moment. 'Goodness me, you'll look like a whole different fella.'

●

As you were passing, Upton cracked the prefect's room portal. 'Can I show you something, Johnny?'

'Uh, sure.'

You stepped inside and he closed the door. A dozen professorial chairs lined both sides of a long, narrow table. He motioned you to join him in one of two reclining corner sofa chairs.

'Nice haircut, Johnny.' He nodded approvingly. 'But what about the other big change?'

'Huh?'

'You never joined the Crusaders.'

'Uh, not my, uh, thing.'

'You don't believe in Jesus?' If Upton's elevation to head prefect had not dented his humility, it had at least heightened his sense of purpose.

'I can, uh, believe.'

'That's great, Johnny, because that's the only thing we have to do.'

'Nothing else?'

'Nothing'—he smiled, wanly—'but there *is* a problem.'

'With believing?'

'Yes. You see, it is possible to *believe* yet not to *know*.'

'Huh?' Was the glazing on those dark eyes a gift from Dr Irwin A. Moon?

'It is possible to *know* that we are sinners, that the wages of sin is death and that the Son of God died on the cross for our sins. It is possible to *know* all this, and still be lost—and still not *believe* it.' He rose and stepped to one of the professorial chairs. 'I *know* this chair will hold me up because it's a good, strong chair—but I don't *believe* it, because, as God uses the word *believe*, you simply cannot believe in a chair while standing up.' He fell back into the seat. '*Now*, I'm *believing* in the chair, now I'm *trusting* myself to it.' He rose again. 'If a doctor says you have cancer and that if he doesn't operate you're doomed to die, how do you believe in him? By agreeing with his diagnosis? No! You *truly* believe when you submit yourself and let him operate.'

The language was pure Moon, but the delivery was unadulterated Upton. Moon was silky smooth, but Upton was colonial toffy. 'If I were to ask, are you a child of God? Have you experienced rebirth? What would you say? Some might say, I just don't know.' He shook his head sorrowfully, side to side. 'If that is your answer, you're standing *beside* the chair. You may have agreed with the diagnosis, but you haven't submitted yourself to the Great Physician. Well, when you *truly* believe, you'll *know*—and you'll know precisely because you believe! Then, you'll be able to say with the Apostle Paul, "I know whom I have believed, and am persuaded that he is able to keep that which I have committed unto him against that day." Believing involves a decision'—he shot you his very best come-to-Jesus glance—'a decision that *you* can make right *now*.'

Synchronicity? Perhaps Upton was the messenger you needed. Perhaps invisible forces were at work. Would you go up in smoke, or would the million volts bypass your body and alight elsewhere? The answer came quickly.

●

'It could be any one of these guys, Johnny.' Ted was excited. 'It might even be you.'

'Me? No! But maybe it's *you*. Maybe you're pointing the finger to shift suspicion.'

Craven appeared and crooked the parental digit.

'Into the arena then, Johnny. The game's up for somebody.'

The shopkeeper, his back to the tall window, eyed the solemn influx of potential criminals. Craven stepped forward. 'I asked you boys to be here this morning because you were officially absent from school yesterday during the hour that a crime, a *theft*, was perpetrated. The culprit was carrying a Boys High cap, and wearing the school uniform.' He turned to the victim. 'That is right, Sir?' The aggrieved one nodded. 'And you got a good look at the fellow?'

'I would recognise him anywhere.'

'Indeed. So let me ask you then to take a close look at each of these boys and to select the offender.'

You were third to last in line for inspection. You snuck a sideways glance. The injured party was peering closely into the upturned faces. That was good. No one looked much like you.

His sharp eyes and foul breath were suddenly in your face. But forget the salvos of nicotine and halitosis. Would the enquiring eyes recognise the new you? Your fate hung in the balance. So did his. He'd seem an idiot if he chose the wrong boy. His gaze, though focused, also seemed a little vacant. Had your haircut thrown him for a loop? What about your threads? Yesterday, you were wearing a charcoal, crewneck, full-sleeved jersey. It was not, strictly speaking, regular school uniform. Today, a regulation grey, V-neck short-sleeved sweater exposed your matchstick arms. Let's be honest, the makeover had not only shaved at least a couple of years from your appearance, it reaffirmed your fresh, frail, childlike innocence.

It was never in doubt. He shook his head from side to side, like an ill-fed, ailing python, then moved to the next suspect. 'No,' he said, finally and confidently, 'it was not one of these fellows.'

If he was wrong about that, he got it right, too. The escapade changed you. Whether for better or worse might be hard to say.

The
Slipper

YOU SAW THE STEEL-TOED BOOT SWING.

'Hey, he's putting in the slipper—look!'

And you heard the thump as it landed.

'Yikes! That must've hurt.'

It was a miserably cold, wet, sunless day. You peered into the pile of muddy warriors now extracting themselves from the sullen ruck that had formed around the heavy pigskin. Dazed and with his hands clasped to his bleeding head, a mud-soaked Maori boy staggered to his feet.

'Did the referee see the actual delivery of the reinforced steel-toe?'

'Unlikely. Our match-winning flanker selects his moments as carefully as his victims.'

'Why can't we win a game without kicking some poor kid in the head?'

'Because cruelty seeks a victim,' said Shell.

'Or maybe Coke just trained him to be a winner.'

'Or maybe he's just a vicious jerk.'

'We all hail from savages.'

'Says who?'

'This fellow Darwin.'

Whatever. Anything was possible. For sure, Coke's first-fifteen lineup routinely included the testicle-grabbing Ginger and gay-bashing Coyle. For the rugby pages of the school magazine Coke put it differently: 'Runting's sorties were often rewarding' and 'What Coyle lacks in size he makes up for in determination.'

'Christ, it's cold!'

'And still raining.'

'And yet another scrum's turned into an ugly scramble for that slimy ball.'

'The game's never gonna get out of the forwards.'

'Yeah—and wow! Talk about ugly, he's going again.'

'Such determination.'

'They're returning the compliment!'

'Fisticuffs! Someone's gonna die out there.'

'Not now—look! The referee's blown the whistle.'

'And he's stalking off the field!'

'Hey, fella, there's still twenty minutes to play.'

'He's not listening. He's called the whole thing off.'

'There'll be a stink about this.'

You turned up your wet collar and trudged back across the soggy paddock.

●

Shell read out the banner headline from the *Manawatu Times*. "Fracas follows as Parorangi's all-Maori team challenges local boys high school." He shook his head. 'Race and religion right up front.'

The headline was indeed a dog whistle. Virtually every high school team had a religious bent. Protestant colleges fielded Protestant teams and Roman Catholic schools fielded their own kind. Protestants were imagined to be rather more gentlemanly, especially those of the private school variety. Catholics were coached and cajoled by fervent missionary priests, for whom a win was a victory for Jesus, Mary and Joseph. Parorangi was exclusively Catholic and exclusively Maori, a double whammy. The suggestion within the headline was that these

Maori boys might just be a bunch of fervent savages not yet ready to join in gentlemanly pursuits.

●

'Coke excelled himself! What a man he is! What a coach! What a competitor! What an inspiration!'

'Come on, Ted—what's all this about?'

'The newspaper editor tried to get to the bottom of the Parorangi match fiasco. The coaches and teams were commanded to visit him. Both headmasters went along, too. The idea was to put everything to rest.'

'You were there?'

'I got it first hand. Can't say who. Everyone's sworn to secrecy.'

'I'm sensing that things went off the rails.'

'Your intuitions are sound. First there was lots of finger pointing. Then Coke said, "Your, uh, fellows are new to the game so they lack strategic thinking skills." The Parorangi coach didn't like that. "It was your, uh, *fellows* who resorted to using their fists and their feet," he said, mocking Coke's toffy accent. "Our boys were merely trying to defend themselves from serious injury." Coke stayed on his high horse. "My fellows *never* need to fight," he said. "They know *how* the game is played, and they know precisely how to *play* the game." The priest turned lobster red. "What they know when they're losing the game," he said, "is how to kick a boy who is down on the ground—and *that* is what you've taught them, Mister Colquhoun." Coke went pale but stayed calm. "No one ever saw—or ever will see—any one of my boys kick anyone." The priest was gonna jump in but Craven got there first. "What we need, gentlemen, surely, is to apply our Christian principles and put this matter to rest." The Parorangi head agreed. "A soft word turneth away wrath," he said. The priest nodded and Coke sniffed. "Kind words are called for," said Craven. "Don't you think, Father?"'

'He called him Father?'

'It softened him. He tugged at his collar and turned to his team.

"Well, boys," he said, "we don't need another fight. Let's turn the other cheek. It was a bad day for everyone, and things just got out of hand. That happens in life some days, boys. So, with your permission"—he glanced to the fellow with the bruised eyes and the bandaged head—"I suggest we our offer the Palmerston team a heartfelt apology." '

'Wow! How did that go down?'

'The Maori boys nodded, and the team captain spoke up. "Sorry," he said. "Was a bad day. We accept our blame. Won't happen again." He was respectful. Both headmasters were happy. Craven shot a look at Coke as if to say, "your turn".'

'And?'

'Coke sniffed, then he turned to the team. "Come on boys," he said. "We've nothing to apologise for, we can all walk through that door right now." '

'And they did?'

'They studied Coke's finger. They mostly couldn't quite believe the order. They all knew the truth. But they traipsed out the door, anyway. Coke did, too.'

'That was the end of it?'

'Not quite. The priest got the last word. He shot a dirty look at Craven—who was speechless, by the way—then he spoke directly to the Parorangi team. "We all see for ourselves, then, exactly the kind of example this coach sets for his team. And so, boys, I ask you to join me in a short prayer." He fell to his knees. They followed him down and bowed their heads. "Oh Lord," he said, "help us to fully forgive each and every one of the poor souls who have been taught to follow in the paths of cruelty and arrogance. And, Lord, we pray to you also to care for the heart and to redeem the soul of the arrogant shepherd who led his flock astray." '

Adventure

YOU SAT IN YOUR LITTLE LAIR adjoining Craven's office recording the comings and goings in the big blue register. Craven's office door opened. He slid into the room, a ream of paper in one hand and a small silver key in the other. He nodded in your direction and pursed his bloodless lips, but said nothing. He stepped to the corner armoire, opened it with the key and laid the papers on an open shelf. Then he closed the door, turned and withdrew the key, crept back into his den and dropped the key into the right-hand drawer of his desk.

Why the weird secrecy?

You waited.

You were alone now.

You stepped into his office.

Curiosity killed the cat.

Information brought it back.

•

'Oh, come on, Johnny!' Ted's grin was a mix of joy and horror. 'You haven't really got hold of copies of the year-end exam papers—I mean, really, have you?'

'I know how to get them. They'll arrive on Friday and sit in the armoire over the weekend.'

'But the building's all locked up then—and the exams start on Monday.'

'Exactly.'

'Oh, I dunno. But nothing's at stake—right? I mean we're all going to university anyway.'

'Non enim sine periculo!'

'Huh?'

'No joy without danger.'

'Yeah, life is dull. That's why no one's done any work. Like you said, we're just filling time.'

'But we don't want to fail these exams, either, right?'

'No. That wouldn't be right.'

'Do we have a choice then?'

'There's a tide in the affairs of men—'

'Which taken at the flood leads on to fortune!'

'Fortune and adventure. Nobody's done this before!'

'Or ever will again?'

'Maybe not.'

You were surprised how simple it was to recruit colleagues to this risky enterprise. The call to adventure doubtless outweighed other considerations. For sure, it unleashed a jolt of adrenaline that quickened the heart and evoked a sense of unfettered free will. To be honest though, you'd not boned up on biology and Cyst had made it plain that he was on your tail, so at least one of those exam papers might just be helpful.

●

'Oh, God, You shoulda been there to see how terrible it was!' This time Ted collared you in the shadows of a College House corridor just before lunch on a dreary August Monday. His grin was lopsided. 'And how absolutely awful it's going to be.'

'What happened?'

'Well, you know about Napier last week?'

'They beat our first fifteen and Coke got peeved.'

'Close but no cigar. Coke got pissed off because we lost a cliffhanger in front of a big crowd in the main city stadium. But that's not what's terrible.'

'It's not?'

'No. You gotta remember we went there with three teams. He held up three fingers. 'The idols of the first fifteen. The strivers of the second fifteen'—he grinned—'of which I was properly elected captain—and the big, clumsy fellas who wound up in the third fifteen.'

'And you all lost?'

'Doesn't matter. What matters is that we were there for the night, and a bunch of us went out on the town to salve our wounds and sate our sorrows.' Of course. Ted was a boarder but lived close enough to go home—and ride the fermented hops—just about every weekend. Even now, his toothpaste breath was tinged with stale ale.

'You did?'

'Yeah, we pickled ourselves in demon water. Then some of us gathered some fluff.'

'Girls—wow! Cigarettes, whisky and wild, wild women.'

'Yeah—but that's not what's terrible.'

'I didn't think so—'

'What's terrible is that some pious blabbermouth snitched. Then it all got back to the ever pious Doctor Craven.'

'Oh, Christ, the head got hold of it? Didn't go down well, I'll bet.'

'No—but that's not what's terrible.'

'So what is?'

'He sent for all of us. We just got out of his office.'

'Everyone? Every member of every team who made the trip to Napier?'

'Yeah.'

'What'd he say?'

'Said he'd heard we'd run shouting through the town, smoking and drinking and affronting the local lassies. He droned on and on in that preachy tone.' Ted tilted his head back, looked down his nose, raised the parental digit and mimicked the uncongenial voice. "I'm ashamed—deeply ashamed—of what happened in Napier. You've disgraced not only yourselves, but the entire school. So punishment must be meted out."'

'The dry old bastard wanted to punish everyone? But what's appropriate? How'd he know who did what?'

'He's might be dry, but he's cunning, too. He said, "I know precisely which of you is guilty, and exactly what it was that you did." He let that sink in then followed up. "An appropriate punishment would be expulsion, but I'm prepared to be lenient. I'm going to let the offenders redeem themselves by becoming witnesses to the truth."'

'Witnesses to truth?'

'Yeah, he's got a religious thing. He said, "I am going to let you prove to me—and to the Almighty—that you fully understand and fully repent the gravity of your disgraceful behaviour. I shall do this momentarily, by asking those boys who offended to step forward. First, however, let me re-emphasise that I already know the names of the boys who were involved in this dreadful behaviour. If they do not immediately step forward they will suffer the further disgrace of expulsion. So, now then, who among you is ready to bear witness?"'

'What happened?'

'First there was dead silence—'

'And then?'

'And then we looked at each sideways for maybe a tenth of a second, and then we stepped forward.'

'You all stepped forward?'

'Just half of us.' 'Then what?'

'He looked up at the sky, then down over his beak, then he said, "I applaud your newfound integrity." Then he made us sinners write our names on a sheet of paper. Then he picked it up and pored over it. Then he looked down his proboscis again, and then he said, "As promised, I shall be lenient. But the punishment will also fit the crime. I shall permit no offender to represent the school in any further rugby match this season." '

'The season's just about over—how terrible is that?'

'It's diabolical. Yes, the season ends one week from this coming Saturday, but it finishes with the Silverstream match at the city oval. Thousands of people will pack the stands to watch. And with our best players gone, our team's gonna go down big time.'

'We lost the best players?'

'Yeah, well, the guys who didn't need to take the medicine were mostly Goody Two-Shoes. We lost better than the ballsiest half of the first fifteen.'

'But we can pull a team together from the second and third fifteens?'

'We lost the brassy half of them, too. Pulling any kind of team together will be hopeless. Kids from lower grades—midgets who'll never in a million years make the first fifteen—are gonna be needed to fill the gaps in the lineup. Silverstream's gonna massacre us.'

'What does Coke say?'

'He's grim and livid, sombre and sullen, peeved and pissed off. He wanted to win that game so-o-o-o badly. He thinks Craven blames him for failing to keep us in line. He thinks Craven punished *him*, too.'

'How do you know?'

'By listening to Coke.' Ted puffed his chest, drummed it with his fists, and fell into Coke's whiny accent. "My team was at the zenith of a season's work. I meticulously selected and developed the best boys. I galvanised those young warriors into a winning unit. I brought them to peak performance for precisely this Silverstream match. The momentum was with me—uh, us." ' Ted turned his palms upward, adopted a basset face and continued in a low, sad tone. ' "Oh, it's too late to back out, so we'll send in a makeshift bunch. But this new crew will never be a true team. They'll be in for a pasting. It'll be a rout.

They and the school itself will be humiliated before the entire city. They'll be the laughing stock of every college team in the country. On the positive side of things, however, when the facts are known—and my goodness I shall make sure that happens—my own reputation will remain untarnished."'

'He said all that?'

'He teaches gym not English, but that was the gist of his mutterings.'

'Whattaya think's gonna happen?'

'It's a no-brainer. At least you and I will be together in the grandstand watching the debacle, not out on the field getting whipped, waxed, clobbered and left to present our throats for Silverstream daggers to sliver.'

Ted was right. With more than half his team gone, Coke had fallen into a foul mood. The impossible challenge of finding eight new recruits—three nimble speedsters for the back line, and five ballsy bone-crushers for the forward pack—left him meandering like a dazed but overtly dutiful zombie. A few days later he'd assembled a ragtag team. Fortunately, the vice-captain of the second fifteen, a teetotaller, was available for the crucial fly-half role, as were two non-imbibing forwards. They might be slow, but one of them was reported to have a good boot, which was just as well, because any points the home team might be lucky enough to put on the board would surely come from penalty kicks. The final five recruits were literal lightweights culled from lower echelon teams. The half-back was particularly tiny. So, too, were the fellows on both wings. You watched with Ted from the College House windows as Coke despairingly put them through their paces. It was not a pretty sight. The star power was patently missing. The replacements truly were second, third, fourth and fifth raters. To be fair, Coke didn't shout at them, just whined away and shrugged his shoulders, as if to say, 'What'd you expect?' It was dispiriting for everyone, even the onlookers. Happily, for the meantime anyway, the shameful Napier carousing was kept as the closest of secrets. The few who knew about it were chosen to cheerlead the Palmerston team.

●

'You're just about as keen on poetry as photography, Apollo. So let me share some lines from William Cullen Bryant, a young man not much older than you when he wrote them.' He reached, not without difficulty, into his vest pocket and extracted a gold-monogrammed, soft, well-worn wallet. He fumbled for a moment, then produced a dog-eared paper. He caught you watching his shaky fingers and dropped the paper on the counter. He knew it by heart. His voice was mellow:

> *So live, that when thy summons comes to join*
> *the innumerable caravan, which moves*
> *to that mysterious realm, where each shall take*
> *his chamber in the silent halls of death,*
> *thou go not, like the quarry-slave at night,*
> *scourged to his dungeon, but, sustained and soothed*
> *by an unfaltering trust, approach thy grave*
> *like one who wraps the drapery of his couch*
> *about him, and lies down to pleasant dreams.*

'Wise words from a mere youth, Apollo. Some said the wisdom had to have come from someone older, someone facing death. But insight comes early to some. And whether the thoughts are his or not doesn't much matter. All that matters is that he trapped a heart on a page.'

Whence the wind bloweth

'AS OF RIGHT NOW, Silverstream still thinks our top team's gonna come roaring onto the field.' Saturday the 24th of August 1957 had arrived all too quickly. Ted tossed his overcoat onto the hard boards of our front row seats in the rickety wooden grandstand, patted his white-rimmed, black-flannel high school blazer, and adjusted the rake of his monogrammed school cap. 'They've no idea of their cakewalk to come,' he said, gazing out onto the spongy green field.'

'Maybe that's good,' said Shell.

'Or maybe not. It's a big crowd'—he glanced back into the grandstand—'they've gathered to see their lads win. But the fruit of their loins is about to be squashed.'

'Maybe they'd just like to be entertained,' said Shell, finger-wiping condensation from within his left lens.

'Then they shall have their wish, cos it's gonna be a Roman spectacle.'

'Indeed,' said Shell, 'so be patient and tough; some day this pain will be useful to you.'

You glanced to the showground clock—3.00 p.m.

'Here they come!'

Kicking up their boots behind them, showing their sprigs and the layer of black polish that had been applied to their soles, thirty of the supposedly brightest stars of the Kiwi college rugby firmament burst onto the field. Nobody cared that the sky was mackerel and the air chilly. All that mattered was to stand, roar and rattle the grandstand.

The two teams came to a twitchy rest facing each other, snorting steamy condensation like stallions. The Silverstream lads were uniformly fit and handsome in their blue-and-white striped jerseys. The Palmerstonians were clad in glowing all-white monogrammed shirts and matching shorts, an immaculate livery reserved exclusively for sacred first-fifteen encounters.

'Seems like an equal matchup—so long as you don't look closely!'

Ted was right. Everything looked okay. Well, kind of. But anyone who actually studied the teams would surely have noted that the local lads seemed a weird blend of the good, the bad and the ugly. Several had not yet shed their baby fat and, compared to their rivals, at least a couple of Palmerston conscripts might have passed for Lilliputians.

The school brass band struck up 'God Save the Queen' and all stood to attention.

'Maybe it shoulda been God Save the Queens,' whispered Ted, as the dirge faded.

Laced with adrenaline, pacing and snorting, the two teams cantered backwards, spreading out across the field in readiness to engage the battle.

The referee, socks hoisted to the knee, neatly clad in ironed pants and shirt, raised his right hand, put the whistle to his lips, drew a deep breath and blew the match to life.

Palmerston had the kickoff. Silverstream nabbed the ball and their fly-half shot a long kick for the line, finding it safely within Palmerston territory.

'Our fellows look okay,' said Shell.

'Yeah, well, they *look* okay,' said Ted, 'but if Silverstream runs the ball, watch out!'

'Oh Christ, they've got it and they're running it. Someone stop 'em!'

'Someone has!'

'One of our midgets—thank heaven for little boys!'

'They've lost the ball—it's dribbling crazily!'

'Look! Look! Look!'

The regular Palmerston inside centre grabbed the bobbling leather—'Go, Palmerston, go!'—he sashayed down the field. Clutching the precious ball, he glanced to his right.

'Yes!'

The teetotalling second-fifteen fly-half was alongside.

'Yes!' The ball was flung.

'Yes!' The muscular Christian grabbed it.

'Yes!'

Ted rolled his programme into a make-believe broadcaster's microphone and mockingly shouted to the four hundred cheering boys in the stand, 'So, aficionados of fine rugby, one of the brightest of the stars who took the field today rose to the occasion, tucked the orb beneath his arm and sprinted like the hound of heaven to the try line, where to the joy of the crowd—which continues even as I broadcast—and the discomfort of this wobbly grandstand, that graceful ball-gatherer gently placed the pigskin on hallowed earth beneath the posts . . . so now the score is'—all eyes swung to the white letters on the modest black scoreboard—

PALMERSTON 3 / SILVERSTREAM 0

'That's right, sports fans, one superb try to the home team and nothing to the visitors . . . and now we await the conversion attempt . . . the kicker is to be a big blond fellow with an infectious smile . . . he's playing in his first ever game for his school'—he winks—'and some say his last . . . he's lining up the ball now . . . he's pacing backwards . . . he's coming in for the kick . . . and there it goes! Oh my goodness, yes, so now the score is—

PALMERSTON 5 / SILVERSTREAM 0

'Yes! So, come on lads!' he rat-a-tat-tatted on the floor boards—'let's hear it—One-Two-Three-Four.'

They all joined in.

'Three-Two-One-Four.'

'Who for?'

'Why for?'

'Who you gonna yell for?'

'P! – N! – B! – H! – S! — School!'

The jam-packed grandstand crowd applauded and Ted returned a mock bow. You fell back onto the raw timber seating.

'Can you believe it?'

Shell grinned. 'I believe it precisely because it is impossible.'

'Oh God, they've pushed us back already.'

'And their tough little half-back is ready to roll—'

The whistle shrieked and the referee's arm went up.

'Oh, God! No! He's awarding a penalty—to *them*!'

'Oh, God, please let them miss that easy kick—'

'God is deaf.'

PALMERSTON 5 / SILVERSTREAM 3

Five minutes gone. The next ten passed even more quickly. Silverstream got most of the possession, but Palmerston was always in the game. You gazed in wonderment. Had that opening whistle called something down from heaven? Had it transformed infants into warriors? Was it because they had nothing to lose? Was it the thrill of finding that the moment was real? Perhaps they truly were treading upon hallowed ground. For sure, they were representing something greater than their puny selves. Hearts were in play. Win or lose, they were on their way to becoming a first-fifteen team whose match would never be forgotten.

To the delight of the crowd Palmerston responded with a sparkling back-run and a bone-crushing forward rush. Deep on defence, but with the ball in hand, Silverstream kicked high and far, intending to find the safety of the touch line.

But that did not happen.

The star of the Palmerston backline cantered forth and caught it, sped through a slew of wrong-footed defenders, drew the fullback, then hurled the ball to an infant recruit whose baby boots seemed never to touch to the turf as he glided unopposed to score the try.

Again the sure foot of the smiling blond recruit sent the ball sailing oh-so-nicely between the uprights.

PALMERSTON 10 / SILVERSTREAM 3

Who could forget that cheering?

Silverstream came back on the attack but got stymied short of the line. Their centre finally burst through and unloaded to the winger, who dived for a try in the corner.

PALMERSTON 10, SILVERSTREAM 6

You owe us, God—so make him miss this sideline conversion.

Thank you!

Silverstream continued to press but the defence was astonishing. If the locals were Lilliputians, Silverstream was Gulliver and the little guys bound him up.

A minute to halftime.

A midfield scrum.

The ball began to emerge.

Palmerston was ready to spring . . .

Oh, no! The referee raised his hand and blew the whistle. Holy shit. An easy penalty for Silverstream.

PALMERSTON 10 / SILVERSTREAM 9

'What'd you think, Ted?'

He shook his head and rolled his eyes. 'Who'd have guessed? Halftime and a one point difference. But we've been lucky. Silverstream'll come back strong and time's on their side.' He touched his cap and glanced backwards. 'Hey, look up there—it's Coke in his All Black blazer.'

'He's with a reporter—they're just watching the players drain their orange slices.'

'He's glum—looks like he sucked a lemon.'

A curtain fell, within a crypt
an ebbing old man curled his lip.
Glory's brief, a mackerel sky,
time's a rascal, laurels lie.

'I was right!' Ted jabbed your rib. 'Silverstream's come back strong.'

'Yeah, but our luck's still holding, they've only looked good. Nobody's scored so we're still winning—and this second half is disappearing in a blur.'

'And victory is becoming ever more visible.' Time and again, just as Silverstream looked like scoring, our Lilliputians sent Gulliver tumbling, sprigs over headgear.

'Our turn! Here comes the ball.'

The whistle shrieked.

'A penalty! To us'—Ted shook his head—'but it's on the halfway line!'

'Hercules himself couldn't heft that wet pigskin through the posts and above the bar.'

Ted jumped to his feet. 'No! No!' he shouted. 'Take the safe choice; kick for the line! . . . Oh no!' He furled his programme into a microphone. 'This unsung lad is lining up an ill-advised attempt to add three points . . . and now . . . Thump! The ball is soaring . . . and the line is true—but will it fall short? . . . and into the arms of the dangerous Silverstreamers? . . . And the answer is . . . No!' He pumped his arms. 'Yes! Yes! Yes!'

PALMERSTON 13 / SILVERSTREAM 9

'Only a converted try can save them, now.'

'And tempus fugit—'

'They're rattled and desperate—'

The whistle shrieks.

'Another penalty kick for us!'

'It's an easy shot—they're history!'

Right he was—

'Per aspera ad astra!'

'Say what?'

'Through difficulties to the stars.'

'Coke's still glum.'

'Of course. It wasn't his team that won. The stars he'd polished never appeared. The guys who did were ones he'd shunned.'

'There were nine changes in the lineup—and eight new faces. Craven showed that Coke had wasted dollops of time—his own and everyone else's—with all his dancy-prancy coaching and strategising. Don't you get it? Coke's been made to look like an idiot. In front of the whole school, too.'

'But he trained the guys who took the field today.'

'But his heart was never in it. He'd have been happier if they'd lost. Then Craven would be the idiot, not him.'

'But doesn't Coke look like a hero, anyway?'

'Only if you didn't know what went down. Face it. Right now, he's just another gym teacher. That's what's getting to him. That's why he's pissed off. And you know what? A wise man does not urinate against the wind.'

Making the most of things

'OH, CHRIST, THE DOOR'S LOCKED!' Ted's whisper echoed down the dark corridor. 'How're we gonna get in?' All eyes turned to you. A happy little band of brothers had welcomed the call to adventure. The quest was on. The examination papers were the sacred parchments. Obstacles had abounded. Breaking into the main building had not been easy. The surly door to Craven's inner sanctum was the final impediment. You pointed to a ventilation window just beneath the ceiling. There was no need for further explanation. They heaved you onto Ted's shoulders. You reached up, clutched the window sill and pulled yourself into the opening. You lowered yourself ever so gently onto the desk below, then slid to the carpet and, after steadying yourself, stepped to Craven's desk. You opened the top right-hand drawer. Oh, Happy Day. You grabbed the key and headed for the armoire. You turned the key in the lock and the door opened. Oh, yes.

●

'*Kiss Me Deadly*, Jimmy. You wanna do it?' She'd not been in her silver cage when you arrived, but she'd caught your eye on the way out. Well, let's be honest, you'd been praying she'd be there. The theatre had been just about empty but the movie was great. *Gone with the Wind*, you'd always wanted to see it. Today was Friday—and nearly half-past five by the clock on the wall behind her pert face. The Monday Labour Day holiday lay ahead. Christmas and freedom were just six weeks away. Most every College House inmate had gone home for the long weekend. Not you. What would be the point? They'd be watching too closely. Better to stay in prison. And then break out. You'd cut classes again today. Nobody noticed. Who cares if they did?

> The physical stimulation given to the male organ by the contact of the female genital area is considerably increased by sexual excitement and desire on her part. The vaginal clasp, in its pillowly softness and delicacy, its intense warmth, is in itself a delight.

'*Kiss Me Deadly*? You're not just kidding, right?'

'Meet me midnight Sunday, Jimmy.' She set her pink tongue to her pearly teeth. 'We'll do it together.' Her eyes sparkled.

●

'I'll be out of town for a week, Apollo, but when I return I'll show you my portfolio.'

'The mystery of your work will be revealed?'

'And this time you'll be the judge.'

'You said we should be our own best critics.'

'Ultimately, as we become more discerning, yes.'

'Do we become increasingly critical, too?'

'One might hope to create a hundred fine photos in a lifetime, but a handful would be more than enough.' He gazed out the door and pointed, shakily as ever. 'Look, Apollo, light is gliding down the street.' The sun had come out from behind a cloud. You both watched it disappear. He turned back to you and took a long, deep breath. 'Even one image can earn a place in posterity.'

'Might you have such a shot?'

'I should be so lucky.'

'Do you at least have a favourite?'

'My favourite'—he set his palms firmly on the counter—'is the one I'm going to take tomorrow.'

●

All eyes of the brave souls who shared the successful rescue of the sacred parchment were on Cyst as he held your completed examination paper in his hand. 'You truly, uh, *surprised* me.' He dropped the neat unblemished pages onto your desk and pointed to them with his manicured forefinger. 'I'm wondering, seriously wondering, how you achieved this.' You sensed your colleagues breathing heavily, especially Ted, whose desk was next to yours. 'So let me enquire a little further.' He pretended to be thinking, but already knew what he wanted to ask. 'What was your place in the English examination?' You remained mute. Given the intermittent nature of the stutter, it was hard for him to say whether you were stuck for something to say or merely stuck for words. At that moment, both states were in play. 'I ask because not only are your answers *profound*'—he seemed to think he was onto a clever line of enquiry—'but each and every sentence you have written is *perfect*.' He was unprepared for your answer.

'Second, Sir.'

'Second? You came second in the English class.'

'Yes, Sir.'

'Hmm. Second?'

Ted jumped in, quietly and respectfully. 'Wareham is *very* good at English, Sir.'

'So you can write a good sentence?'

'Yes, Sir.'

'Well that is something, I suppose. And yet, and yet . . . and yet I am still left gasping at the cogency of the entire paper. It is almost, if I may say so, Master Wareham, almost as if you had somehow managed to *copy* the answers out of an *encyclopaedia*.'

'Yes, Sir.'

'Yes, you say? What does that mean?'

'He means, Sir, that it might indeed seem as if he had copied the answers, Sir.'

'Might it indeed? And why might that be?'

'Because he swotted up for the exam at the last moment, Sir. We all did, Sir. Looked back over the course work, then grabbed the encyclopaedia and burned the midnight oil the night before the exam, Sir.'

'That still doesn't explain—'

'Wareham's not like other people, Sir.' The adventurers nodded in agreement. 'He also has a photographic memory. He can see a page and make himself remember the whole thing, right down to the commas and everything. It seems uncanny, Sir, but I gather it's not unusual with people like him.'

'Let him rewrite a paragraph right now then.'

'That would be unfair, Sir. The exam was last week. He only needed to keep the pages in his head for a few hours. It'll all be gone now.'

Midnight

YOU SLIPPED OUT THE WINDOW and onto the fire escape. The air was warm and the sky starry. Descending the thin steel rungs of the narrow steel ladder in street shoes while wearing long grey trousers and a donegal jacket was not easy. You dropped the final eight feet and landed on the glistening moist grass. You crouched and held your breath. All College House lights were out. Only chirping crickets broke the silence. You checked your watch. You'd be there on time. Would she?

> *Entangled in a shining field*
> *I caught your moonlight glance*
> *reflecting from a golden shield,*
> *and not, you said, by mere mischance.*

You couldn't miss her, not in that tight-waisted, ming blue dress with neon lime buttons, neck to knee. Matching pump shoes, too. Her smile was warm. 'Come on, Jimmy, I've got the tickets already.' She grabbed your hand and pulled you into the theatre. It was already nearly full and excitement was in the air. Finding a seat wasn't easy. You wound up on the side and near the front. The screen was close. You liked that.

'It's the perfect movie, Jimmy.'

'A lot of people seem to think so.'

'Yeah, midnight movies often pull a full house. The locals are starved for excitement and it's the only game in town.' The lights dimmed and credits appeared. As she squeezed your hand her cherry lips turned to ruby. '*Kiss Me Deadly*'—she smiled a sisterly smile and pecked your cheek—'let's see what you make of it.'

'You've seen it already?'

'Yeah, but I wanted to share it with you.'

'I'm glad.'

'You seem very glad.'

'I'll tell you why later.'

You were happy, too. It would be a treat to see Mickey Spillane's characters on the big screen. She'd be surprised, shocked even, to hear that you'd met the author himself. He was fun. But let's be honest. That was nothing compared to the thrill of anticipating what might come next. You glanced into her sparkling eyes:

> *We'll share a mystic jubilee,*
> *and tango in a cloud of dreams;*
> *we'll skip to chords we cannot flee,*
> *and waltz upon voltaic beams.*

●

'Come on'—she grabbed your hand as you exited the theatre—'I'm on my own this weekend. And you're not in a hurry, right?'

You studied the fluorescent-lit faces within the milling crowd. Nobody recognised you. That was good.

'Might as well be hung for a sheep as a lamb.'

'No one's gonna hang you. It's a quarter to two now, and you don't have to be back until when?'

'I've got until breakfast. I can pretend I got up early and went for a walk.'

'We'll find a way to while away the hours. There's lots to talk about.'

'Lots.'

The moonlit street was quiet. So were you both. She reached up and unlatched the hasp on the gate. You stepped through it and the soft gravel crackled. You caught the scent of the oak. The tree itself was lost in a black shadow.

'You like the new poster, Jimmy? And the girl in the leopard-skin pants?'

'I guess. What do you like about it?'

'The film noir funk. A guy and a girl on a couch. One arm around her, a revolver draping from the other—'

'She's looking to be kissed?'

'Kick off your jacket and shoes and jump on the bed, Jimmy. Then read what she's saying. I'll be back with cocoa and macaroons.' She bounced out of the room. You lay back on the feathery eiderdown and studied the tag-line in the box above the brunette's hair. Wild, indeed.

She set the tray alongside you on the bed. Steam rose from the chocolate milk and disappeared into the soft bedside light. She kicked off her pumps, gingerly positioned herself next to you and raised her blue mug. 'Here's to adventures.' She watched as you sipped. It was a magic moment. The macaroon was every bit as delicious as the cocoa, but nowhere near as lovely as her smile. 'So what about the poster, Jimmy. What's she saying?'

'Like I said, seems she wants him to kiss her.'

'The words in the box above her head—"I don't care what you do to me, Mike, just do it fast"—they give the totally wrong impression. She's talking about ending her life, not jumping into bed.'

'Hmm. It's, uh, cleverer than I thought.'

'So, what'd you think of the movie?'

'What would you say if I told you I met the author of the book?'

'You met Mickey Spillane? Are you saying that you really did meet him?! Well then, I say *"Go on,* you did *not!"*'

'Yeah, but I did. He was passing through on a trip. I met him at Whitcombes. He was looking for copies of his own books. Maybe lots of authors do that. He was nice. We spoke for a while, then he invited me back to the Empire for a milkshake.'

'Mickey Spillane, eh? What was he wearing?'

'Denim—jeans and a jacket—and a white tee-shirt.'

'How old was he?'

'I dunno. Fortyish, maybe.'

'Hmm. So maybe it really was him.'

'It really was.'

'What'd you talk about?'

'Writing and religion, mostly.'

'Writing. He knows about writing?'

'His books are selling zillions.'

'The character is selling the books, not the author.'

'Maybe, but it was Mickey Spillane who created Mike Hammer.'

'Not really.' She grabbed a paperback from her bed table. 'Mickey Spillane stole this 1920s writer's private-eye character, Race Williams. Stole the cover, too, see. Same idea, anyway. Race Williams was brutal, violent, hard-talking, illiterate—and loyal. Spillane stole the character right off the page. Listen, Jimmy:

> *Sometimes . . . one hunk of lead is worth all the thought in the world . . . I never bumped off a guy who didn't need it . . . You can't make a hamburger without grinding up a little meat.'*

She pretended to roll her eyes then smiled. 'But if Race Williams was a killer, he wasn't a crook. Just like Mike Hammer, he was a good guy ridding the world of bad guys.'

'You're really into this stuff.'

'I love all of it. Stories show the way and characters show the heart.'

'So what'd we learn tonight?'

'Only that Mike Hammer has no heart. Right at the opening, he's recklessly barrelling down the freeway. He winds up tracking down a Commie conspiracy and a Pandora's box. The end of the world is at hand! "I don't care how you kill me, Mike, just end my life before you open that terrible box." So will he flip the lid? The book sold zillions and the theatre was full because Mike Hammer is tougher than us and he'll do anything—*anything*—to save us from danger in a rotten world. Even the credits ran upside-down. But you know what's really funny? What's really funny is how the whole thing mirrors Mickey Spillane's crazy religion. I mean you know he's a Jehovah's Witness, right?'

'He told me.'

'He did? What'd he say?'

'Just what you said—he uses his books to witness what's happening in the world.'

'That was it? And he said "witness".'

'He said the reader would get a surprise when Mike Hammer, who seemed like a sleazebag, turned out to be a good guy saving the world from evil people.'

'See Jimmy, that's it! Spillane just promotes his robotic religion. The crooks he shoots are never human, just devils without feelings. He needs to rid them from the world to create his silly Jehovah notion of paradise.'

'You're sure?'

She jumped from the bed and grabbed another paperback from her vanity table. 'Listen to what he writes:

I snapped the side of the rod across his jaw and laid the flesh open to the bone. I pounded his teeth back into his mouth with the end of the barrel . . . and I took my own damn time about kicking him in the face. He smashed into the door and lay there bubbling. So I kicked him again and he stopped bubbling.'

'Kind of, um, violent—'

'Oh, Jimmy! He's not talking about a dying man *bubbling*, he's talking about a devil *Beelze*-bubbling! Spillane's a true-blue, right-wing religious nut. He only ever sees the world in terms of good and evil.' She tossed the book back to the vanity table. 'Like most of those nitwits he's a hypocrite, too!'

'You think?'

'He stole the character, Jimmy. I bet he knows he did it, too. I bet deep down he feels guilty. I bet he knows he's not the real deal. I bet that's why he pretends to be so tough.' She paused and took a deep breath. The soft bedroom light danced ever so gracefully over her sallow complexion. She grinned. 'You wanna play real-deal?'

'Real-deal? Don't think I know the rules.'

'But I do—so let's play a hand of real-deal *I, the Jury*. I'll be the evil Doctor Charlotte Manning, you can be Detective Hammer.'

'After what you said about him, I'm not sure I want to be Mike Hammer.'

'You can be you, then.'

'The reader inside Mike Hammer's skin?'

'Exactly.'

'But you'll still be a cold-blooded femme fatale?'

'Beneath Doctor Charlotte Manning's outerwear I'll still be me.'

'Sounds, uh, exciting.'

'Did you ever undress a girl?'

'Uh. Not that I, uh, remember.'

'You'd remember. So here's the game.' She pressed her palms under her breasts and pointed to the lime buttons. I need to get comfortable, Mike. Undo these.'

Was she kidding? Her eyes said no. And more. 'Do whatever you want to me, but do it fast.'

The buttons fell open. Her breath was warm. The blue sea of her sleek dress parted. She was wearing nothing else. 'Touch me, Mike. Touch me now.' Her breasts were full, firm and silky. She was breathing faster. She set her hands to your shirt, peeled back the buttons, then pressed her palms to your chest. Her mouth was soft, her tongue sweet. You fell back on the bed. She touched herself. 'Watch me, Mike, watch.' You did as told. Gosh she was beautiful. In the bedside light her breasts turned crimson. 'Now, Mike. Now Jimmy—whoever you are and whatever you want. Now. Press. Yes. Now.'

You were five years old. Von took you to the circus. At the close of the evening a pretty girl in white tights sat atop a glistening horse. Catching your eye, she nudged the animal close and beckoned you to touch it. Then she grabbed you around the waist, hoisted you onto the saddle in front of her and fixed you in a harness. Starting slowly, she rode the beast around the ring. The hooves of the mount thumped the damp sawdust and the crowd roared. Faster and faster you went, then, with a shift that sent a jolt of adrenaline, the horse burst into a canter. The pretty rider loosed her grip and you began to levitate. Wires attached to your harness were being tugged by somebody. Like an eagle, you glided in dizzying circles above the upturned faces of the crowd.

You dressed quietly and stepped to the window. The moon was waning. Dawn was not far off. She stirred in the bed, gathered the sheet to her neck, and sat up. 'You're going now, Jimmy?'

'I have promises to keep.'

'And miles to go before you sleep? Oh, Jimmy, I'm gonna miss our little talks.'

'Miss our talks? Why?'

'I'm heading off.'

'Heading off?'

'I'm going to New York. The bookings are all made. I go tomorrow.'

Your head spun.

'You're leaving?'

'I'm *going*, not *leaving*.'

Her words failed to quell your confusion.

'There's a difference?'

'There's a big difference. You're part of me now. You'll always be wherever I go. We're characters in a movie we created. It'll play inside our heads forever.'

Her intensity was beguiling. Hypnotic, even.

'We're dancers on a Grecian vase?'

'Better. We're still alive and we know what happened. We can rerun the movie whenever we want.'

'What's in New York?'

'Civilisation, Jimmy—life!'

'More than's here?'

'What's here, Jimmy, is British movies, American movies and French movies. Which is the truer world, theirs or ours? Palmerston's a bowl with no goldfish. I need an ocean or I'm gonna die.'

'We'll share no more movies?'

'We'll share every movie that ever was or will be. Whenever I see a movie I'll think of you. I do now.' Was she mimicking Spillane or merely continuing the game of real-deal? No. In that moment you saw her in a whole new light. This was pure Veronica. You might have been a mere distraction for her, but she was the real deal for you. Was it love you felt? Puppy love or actual love? Maybe there's no difference. 'Listen, Jimmy, I'd stay in this bowl just to be around you. I'd stay because we're a match. But we're a weird match. An out-of-this-world, once-in-a-lifetime match. But we're just not a real-world match. We can never be that. You're sensitive and smart. But you're a boy. I'm not that much older, but I'm a woman. You noticed? You look lost, Jimmy. Lost but not forlorn. I love that mix of vulnerability and courage. It's, uh, potent. So kiss me again before you go, before we both go. What's the time? You've got time. We'll create a great ending. We'll do it right here and right now. It'll play forever. Come on.'

Memory loss

YOU'RE NOT HERE, VERONICA, yet you still surround me. How does that work, actually? Not very well.

Telepathy, though fine and right,
will not, alas, procure delight.

•

'Secrets are safe, chaps,' said Ted. 'Cyst has accepted that Johnny possesses a photographic memory.'

'It was an inspired defence,' said Shell. 'An appealing image, perfectly developed.'

'Very funny—but Johnny's English exam performance was the clincher. Just as well we filched that paper too.'

'I got that for you guys. I only needed biology.'

'Yeah. Biology. Who cares about chlorophyll and frogs? Anyway, it doesn't matter. The year's just about over and we can forget about all that stuff.'

'Photographic memories will vanish?'

'I already know *nothing*.'

'Me too. What happened?'

•

Yeah, whatever happened? Trouble was you could forget nothing—
and went searching for everything.

> *Could've sworn I saw you, Veronica:*
> *I could've sworn I saw you in the square.*
> *But I of course was wrong, it was not you.*
> *No surprise there, my petalled sweet and fair*
> *—no smile and no delight, no, nothing new.*

●

'The little courtroom was overflowing, not entirely surprising for a
Saturday morning drama.' Shell almost looked like a young lawyer
himself. Blazer, greys, white shirt, school tie—the full works. 'I got a
place just outside the door and heard everything.'

You grabbed the Ping-Pong ball out of the air and halted the game.
Ted set his paddle onto the table. 'And?' He raised both hands, inviting
Shell to share everything.

'And the verdict's in, chaps.'

'How'd it play out?'

'Bear in mind that it took an hour for the beak to make his summary
to the jury.'

'Yeah—but what was the final scoreboard?'

'If you don't mind, I'll answer your first question first.'

'Okay—how *did* it play out then?'

'First, his honour said that free speech is mostly okay and fair
criticism is to be expected, but it has to be honest, and directed at the
book, not the author—then he added that innuendo can be just as
damning as plain language.'

'Sounds like a referee peeing down both legs.'

'Then he got specific. Said Wilson had a warped line of thinking
on religious subjects.'

'He said that?'

'*Very* warped, is what he said, actually. Then he hinted that Wilson
might just be a dirty man with a dirty mind—'

'Wow!'

'Then he put the knife back into the sheath. Wilson's mind on matters of obscenity and religion might just be irrelevant, he said, for the core issue was whether such character flaws prove that Wilson deliberately used his fictional character to attack our sacred Board of Governors. If not, then the newspaper headline was libellous, and if so, damages would be in order.'

'So then what happened?'

'The jury retired and came up with a verdict—'

'And, come on now, what was that?'

'Spoils to the victor. Wilson won the day and the jury awarded damages.'

You lobbed the celluloid to Shell. 'Come on, now!' He caught the ball and folded it into his hand.

'How much?' said Ted

'"How poor they are that have not patience!" Okay then'—he raised both hands as if to command an orchestra, but with a five-star Barna Ping-Pong ball instead of a baton—'The jury found for the plaintiff and awarded him one thousand, five hundred New Zealand pounds.'

'Wow.'

'He was seeking another thousand, actually. But this was a good outcome; nearly a year of salary.'

'Wilson 1500–*Manawatu Times* nil.'

'The *Times* did worse than nil. They'll also have to pay Wilson's costs, and court costs.'

'So it was a drubbing.'

Shell rolled the ball back along the table to you.

'I guess you could say that.'

That was your profile, right, Veronica?
I passed your movie house the other day
and caught your contour just inside the door,
your smile beyond the line of my survey
—or so it seemed, as I said heretofore.

The door was shut and the lights were off. You put your nose to the window pane. Someone was in there rummaging around. The door opened and a pair of pince-nez glasses peered out. 'You're looking for something?'

'I was, uh, looking for, uh, Vincent.'

'I'm afraid Vincent is, uh, gone.'

'Gone?'

'He took a turn and went to hospital.'

'Gone?'

'He gave up the ghost.'

'Huh?'

'He stopped eating. It was a choice.'

'Did he, uh, say, uh, why?'

'Do you really want to know? Are you okay? Well then, what he said was, "If this is dying, Apollo, I don't think much of it."'

'Apollo?'

'You know this fellow?' He tucked his thumbs into his waistcoat. 'Okay, I get it. We thought he was hallucinating but apparently not. He said Apollo was a god of light and a College House kid. So *you're* Apollo, right? Yes of course, you fit the rest of the description perfectly. Well, truth be told he's gone where we're all going. But before he set off he dictated a letter for you and had it sealed up in an envelope. I have it out back. He said you might drop by. If not, I was to find a way to get it to you. And if I couldn't do that, I was to burn it.'

But no, it was not you, Veronica.
Alas, it was not you, not you at all.
And so I wandered down the street
considering the fateful curtain call
that fell to guillotine you at my feet.

Tea and sympathy

A PREP SCHOOL BOY struggles with his sexuality and finds comfort in the company and compassion of the wife of the boy's housemaster.

Something about that movie tagline captured your attention. The new cashier was a dour creature with warts and a moustache. Shouldn't you be at school, her beady eyes asked. Inside your head, Veronica's voice sounded softly. 'Sit back and relax, Jimmy. The best movies are the ones we create inside our heads, so I think you're gonna love this one. The omens are good—big wide CinemaScope screen and lovely melancholy Metrocolor. Deborah Kerr is playing the wife, who beneath her tweeds is kind of sexy. Does she look like anyone you know? Coke's wife, Betty, right? Leif Erikson is the husband, a mindless macho male—just like Coke, yes? John Kerr is the prep school boy, a lost soul—just like guess who? Hold my hand, Jimmy. Here we go—'

> COKE: Look, Betty, when I brought you here a year ago I told you it was a tough place for a woman with a heart like yours. I told you you'd run across boys, big and little boys, full of problems, problems which for the moment seem gigantic and heartbreaking. And you promised me then you wouldn't get all taken up with them. Remember?

BETTY: Yes.

COKE: When I was a kid in school, I had my problems, too. There's a place up by the cricket field where I used to go off alone Sunday afternoons and cry my eyes out. I used to lie on my bed just the way that John does, listening to phonograph records hour after hour. . . .

There's a history to all men's lives.

But I got over it, Betty. I learned how to take it.

Don't believe him, Betty. Come away with me . . .

When the headmaster's wife gave you this teapot she told you what she tells all the new masters' wives. You have to be an interested bystander. Just as she said, all you're supposed to do is every once in a while give the boys a little tea and sympathy.

That would be lovely.

BETTY: Why should my interest in this boy make you angry?

COKE: I'm not angry.

BETTY: You're not only angry. It's almost as though you were, well, jealous.

COKE: Oh, come on now.

BETTY: Well, how else can you explain your vindictive attitude towards him?

COKE: Jealous! I know you like to be different, just for the sake of being different . . . And I like you for it . . . But this time, lay off. Show your fine free spirit on something else.

BETTY: On something that can't hurt us?

COKE: All right. Sure. I didn't mind putting it that way. And Betty?

BETTY: Yes?

COKE: Seeing John so much . . . having him down for tea alone

. . . I think you should have him down only when you have the other boys . . . For his own good, I mean. Did you ever consider that you're responsible for his acting up?

BETTY: Yes, I am responsible, but not as you think. I try to help by being nice to him, by being affectionate. By showing him he's liked . . . yes, even loved. He has to prove to bullies, bullies like you, Coke, that he's a man . . . Well . . . I just wish he would prove it with me.

COKE: What in Christ's name are you saying?

BETTY: Yes, I shock you. But you're right, I *am* responsible. My heart cries out for this boy. I want to help as one human being to another.

COKE: You pity him.

BETTY: No, my heart in its loneliness cries out for this boy . . . cries out for the comfort he could give me too.

COKE: You don't know what you're saying. We'll discuss this, if we must, later on . . .

BETTY: There'll be no later on, Coke. I'm leaving you.

COKE: Over this thing?

BETTY: Yes this thing, and all the other things in our marriage.

COKE: For God's sake, Betty, what are you talking about?

BETTY: I'm talking about love and honour and manliness and tenderness and persecution. I'm talking about a lot. You haven't understood any of it.

COKE: What haven't I understood?

BETTY: You call this boy a stuttering fairy . . . In fact, this boy is more of a man than you are. Manliness is not all swagger and swearing and mountain climbing. Manliness is also tenderness, gentleness, consideration. You men think you can decide who is a man, when only a woman can really know . . . I did love you,

Coke. But not just for your outward show of manliness, but because you needed me . . . For one unguarded moment you let me know you needed me, and I have tried to find that moment again the year we've been married. . . . Why did you marry me, Coke? In God's name, why? You've resented me. Almost from the day you married me you've resented me. You never wanted to marry, really. . . . Did they kid you into it? Does a would-be headmaster have to be married? Or what was it, Coke? You would have been far happier going off on your jaunts with the boys, having them to your rooms for feeds and bull sessions . . . I became a wife without privileges . . .

COKE: You did not become a wife.

BETTY: I know. I know I failed you. In some terrible way I've failed you.

COKE: You were more interested in mothering that little queen than in being my wife.

BETTY: But you wouldn't let me know. You wouldn't let me.

COKE: What do you mean I wouldn't let you?

BETTY: Did it ever occur to you that in mocking that boy you persecute in him the very thing you fear in yourself?

You're to blame, Veronica.

It was sin and you're to blame.
You torched me in a wicked game,
you set my heart and soul aflame,
—a fire with no insurance claim

While I was blinded with desire
you bound me up with baling wire,
stacked me on a funeral pyre,
then set a match and lit my fire

But here in hell, where love's taboo,
where sinners' debts at last fall due,
where memory's all that I'm wise to,
I thirst for one more taste of you.

You are a temptress and to blame
I'll always love you, just the same.

A knock on the darkroom door. Betty! The door closed tight upon her rush of perfume. Her eyes sparkled beneath the dim red bulb. 'I came to say goodbye, John.' Her voice was soft, her breath sweet. 'I'll probably never see you again. I'm leaving Coke'—she was breathing heavily— 'for a lot of reasons.' She set her slim fingers to the top button of her silk blouse. 'But before I leave'—one by one she peeled the buttons; she was braless; her pert breasts glowed in the soft red light—'I want you to know'—her skirt fell to her feet—'for your own comfort'—she kicked off her pump shoes and stood completely naked—'that you're more of a man'—she grasped your throbbing member—'now than he ever was'—she leaned back against the door and closed her eyes, and the angel entered heaven—'or ever will be.' She wrapped you with her slim, svelte legs, drew you into her and pushed her warm, moist mouth to your ear. 'Years from now, John . . . When you talk about this . . . and you will . . . be kind.'

Cliffs

YOU WANDERED TO THE TOWN SQUARE, entered the garden and found a soft grassy spot to sit. You contemplated the blue ink inscription on the cream envelope:

APOLLO
(Engagingly Hesitant College House Student)

The handwriting was too perfect to be Vincent's, but the tactful description was his voice for sure. You slid your thumbnail under the flap. As you extracted the cream pages, you caught a zephyr blend of perfume and antiseptic. If a train passed through the square, you never heard it. Nor did you catch the sound of birds or passing cars. You were oblivious also to the neat Courier typeface. You heard only Vincent's mellow voice.

My dear Apollo:

This letter, like a photo, is an attempt to capture a fleeting moment. My wife died a couple of years ago and then my health got shaky. As it got worse I got lonelier, so it was a good day when you walked into my little shop. You gave me lots to think about, more than you realise. These last months have been hellish. My sight has been failing. Taking photos became a challenge, and getting something worthwhile seemed impossible. It was time to move on. We all have to figure out what we want from this absurd world. We take photos because we want to capture moments and make sense of things. Listen to me, Apollo! There is no love other than deeds of love, no genius other than in works of art. Beyond that there is nothing. Action creates both art and reality. We create our own portraits. So create the future you want, Apollo. Don't let anyone tilt you into chasing anything else.

Your friend,
Vincent

●

'Depression is Satan's fee. He demands payback for every drop of wicked pleasure he tempts you to taste. Life becomes rife with feelings of hopelessness, abandonment, confusion, brain-pain and sorrow. The sinner feels so alien to everyone that death can seem preferable to life.'

●

To stand on a cliff and feel the temptation to jump. Sure, that moment provokes anxiety and even dread, but it can be comforting, too:

Lean, lean, lean
Lean a little further, further, further
*   says the echo, echo, echo*
Now hold your breath
and close your eyes
and in the dark
beneath the cliff,
catch the music
of the sea upon the rocks.
Now see the foam that boldly curls,
And there it is!

A soothing couch,
a bed that is the sea,
    with pillows proud
    and soft white sheets
    turned neatly back,
    as if to beckon thee.
Now catch the echo, friend.
Now catch the echo, friend.
Now catch the echo, echo, echo.

●

'I would've asked Jack to massage it for me but he'll be at work for the next three hours.' The Cigarilloed One was yapping at you from the master bedroom, moaning about a knot in her back. She always had a health issue. Aching bunioned toes at one end, regurgitation issues at the other, usually after devouring a carton of chocolates.

She'd thrown off the bedcovers. Clad only in her red rayon night dress, she lay face down on the unmade master bed.

Whatever happened to that ancient, fat-tyred bicycle?

The odours from the potion-laden vanity unit failed to overpower the turd-brown stubs on the bedside table. 'I just need you to pat some of that massage oil on your hands and rub it in behind my shoulder.'

The frame was scabrous, the handle bars bent, the rubber grips sticky.

'Uh'—a weird feeling welled in your stomach—'okay.' You stepped to the side of the bed, dabbed your fingers into the jar of slime, and pressed your hands between her shoulder blades.

The inner tube showed through the bald tyres.

A faint breath of air rustled the curtain that covered the bedroom picture window.

'No, not there, to the left and down a little.'

'Uh, okay.'

'Ooohh—that's better.' She arched her back and your hand slid to the jellylike flesh that encased her ribs. 'Oh, yes, that's much better,' she gurgled, 'just needs more of the same.'

Who would ever want to sit upon that shabby leather?

You caught sight of the scene—and yourself—in the oval vanity mirror.

Send it on to oblivion and run for your life.

You felt a burst of nausea and reflexively halted the ministration. You plucked your fingers from the slimy, flaccid flesh and headed out the door.

●

You enclosed the Jag within the garage and shut out the world. No one could get in, and nothing would escape. Just to be clear, you were not depressed. Yeah, sure, those wretched priests could leave you feeling down. Other people could, too, of course, especially family. You weren't crazy, either. Just lonely, maybe. But not in this moment. Right now you felt relief. No doubt about it, you were now fully in charge of your own destiny. There seemed to be no point in waiting. Home exists, right? It's on the other side of the looking glass. Just have to jump. You connected the tube to the exhaust then fed it in through the passenger window, wound it up and sealed the gap with a strip of rubber foam. Then you eased back into the driver's seat. Home is the place where, when you have to go there, they have to take you in. Home, my friend, comes at the end. It really was time. You reached forward and hit the ignition switch. The engine burst to life and purred. Sickly fumes entered the cabin. So this is what it's like. Not too bad, really. The smell's unpleasant but who cares? Not you. Well, maybe a little. Fumes are clinging to your throat and climbing up into your brain. It's all kind of weird. Angels are not showing up to save you. But wait, who's this?

Recovered memories

'YOU DON'T RECALL OUR COLLOQUY?'

'No. Who are you?'

'Puh-lese, Johnny, I'm *God*.' So, the one and only Master of the Universe truly is a grey-headed old man in gleaming white robes. 'We met a few years ago. We had a long talk just before I sent you down to earth.' His eyes are as bright as the pearly smile within his beard. 'And now we'll need to have that discussion all over again.' Even the voice is Godlike. 'I had a mission for you down there.' He let that sink in. 'And I *sent* you there. But you *screwed up*. Your mission is *not* complete. You also bungled our deal. You were only meant to have one earthly life. But I'm a nice guy with a good heart, so I'm gonna give you a second shot.' He sounded testy, actually. 'Now, as mentioned, there are countless wonders to behold: beautiful women, delicious wines, top cuisine, great plays and music that ranges from the hellish to the heavenly.' He smiled. 'So, sure, enjoy everything. Unfortunately'—he drew a deep breath—'I need to remind you of a couple of problems. First, unless you complete your mission your life on earth will be meaningless to you, and worthless to me—you understand that, right?'

'I, uh, think so, yes.'

'Okay then. So, second, you'll not remember either of our conversations.'

'They'll go the way of episodes of *Mission Impossible*? You'll destroy the tape? So why talk to me at all?'

'Careful, Johnny! Curiosity is a heavenly quality, but it can create a hell of a lot of trouble down on earth. All you need to know is that I've imprinted your mission within your heart. So, down there, heartache is the signal that you're off course. I'll drop in again from time to time to check your progress.'

'You really can be in two places at once?'

'Yes and no. I can't leave my post up here, but I can prod other people to get you a message.' He moved a step closer. 'Okay. Once more into the breach, dear friend. The time is at hand—but first, I must repeat my confession'—his voice dropped a semiquaver—'and my warning.'

'If you really are God, why do you need to confess?'

'Oh, Johnny—I need to confess because, well, I, uh'—he glanced to his silver-sandalled feet—'sometimes make mistakes. Placing souls with compatible families isn't easy, you know. It's damned difficult actually. So my, uh, hit rate has been, well, uh, not too good.'

'You send souls to the wrong families?'

'Yeah'—he looked a tad abashed—'I do my best, but sometimes, well, uh, often actually, I come up short.'

'And people get peeved?'

'They seldom notice, actually. The moment a new soul opens his eyes he typically finds himself looking into the eyes of people who think they own him. A mother coos, "*my* baby". A father calls, "*my* son". They just don't understand that everyone's a unique soul on a special mission. Now listen closely. Here, once again, is the warning. The world's jam-packed with unhappy mortals who failed to complete their missions. They got distracted and failed to heed their aching hearts. So now these lost souls will push *you* to fulfil *their* missions. Do not—I repeat do *not*—fall into that trap. Remember'—his eyes shone brightly—'your own unique personal mission—the fulfilment of *that*—is the only thing that will ever matter.' He pumped a fist and grinned. 'Now, if you'll be so kind as to follow me.' You floated to a huge, silver contraption. 'This is the selfsame celestial slingshot as before, Johnny.' Two winged attendants appeared and hovered alongside the silver pouch. 'Okay then!' The angels turned you upside down and strapped you into position. God raised a chequered flag with one hand and saluted with the other. 'This time, now!'—he dropped the flag and the attendants released the slingshot—'Go tread the path that thou shalt ne'er return!'

Part Four

Revelations

A favour

Mark Alter, Ph.D.
230 Park Avenue
New York, N.Y. 10017

Dear Mark:

I recently received an e-mail asking me to deliver 'a few inspiring words' about my school days to a bunch of boys from our old alma mater who'll be visiting New York in a month or so.

I was conflicted. Given what went down, should I even attempt to deliver such a speech? If so, should I confess what happened? Probably not. Why stir things up? But truth is important, so maybe the fates wanted me to share the whole kit and caboodle.

To clear my head, I set some stuff to paper. I didn't intend to write a memoir, but that's what it turned into. I'm sharing it with you now because I need a favour.

My publisher wants to run with the enclosed unsanitised pages, but I'm in two minds. You attended that school and you're both a writer and a psychologist, so I'd value your collegial opinion on the picture you see in the mosaic and whether you think I should omit or recast some issues. Needless to say, I'll hold the decision to publish—and what to say to these boys—until I hear back from you.

All blessings to you, come what may . . .

John

An opinion

Dr Mark Alter
230 Park Avenue,
New York, New York, 10017

Dear John:

I'm flattered you've entrusted me to offer a 'collegial opinion'. I'm unsure of precisely what you're looking for, but I'm happy to share the picture that emerges for me from your colourful mosaic of characters and events.

First, that you suffered depression following the 9/11 tragedy is unsurprising. The assault on your city heightened—to put it mildly—the apprehension of death we all feel as we grow older. Then the passing of the little dog that shared that experience would aggravate feelings of existential loneliness. So your memoir seems an attempt to create and pass along purpose and meaning, and thereby live on, maybe even join the ranks of the immortals. Good luck with that!

As to the content, some readers may be turned off by the dreamlike structure and erratic, stream-of-consciousness style, but it worked for me, opening, as it did, a window on unresolved past issues that likely sabotage your here-and-now happiness.

Some of the characters you describe seem both vicious and vengeful—traits that the passage of time may well have been reinforced—so you might shade things before you publish, which, by the way, I advise against, since the boy you describe—your own precious self, no less—doesn't always come off too well, either. Critics might indeed accuse you of shameless self-indulgence and attempting to settle old scores. An elegant way to preempt such detractors would be to recast the entire saga as a novel. Such a subterfuge might prove more profitable, too. Your tale might just have universal appeal and fit rather neatly into the coming-of-age genre. You might even contend for literary laurels.

Knowing you as I do, however, I'm guessing you'll resist such devilish temptations and insist on hurtling headlong down the memoir lane. If so, you might omit the homosexual side of things, such goings on being the norm in single-sex schools. That said, you might also give serious thought to whether these assaults upon your childhood self had longer-term effects than even now you apprehend. I note the acid you shower upon Catholic priests, for example. Perhaps your infant antennae detected the levels of underlying hypocrisy that have only recently come fully to light. If so, you've showcased that precocious blend of intuition and wisdom that children so often possess. You might ponder, however, whether your rage against them—and just about every other authority figure in your life—might spring from their failure to protect you from the aforementioned homosexual assaults.

Some people might also advise you to safeguard your acceptability by omitting *all* the sexual stuff—though I personally found it entertaining and, again, revelatory.

The stammering issue was intriguing. I doubt that anybody knew what was going on inside your mind and heart. It made you seem singular, of course, and I guess it cemented the outsider status in which you seem to revel. These days we know that stammering is innately a physiological problem and therefore impervious to psychotherapy. That it can *confer* psychological issues, however, is apparent in what you have written. That said, as things have turned out, that stammer also seems to have been something of a gift, adding not just to your vocabulary, but to your creativity.

Your parents are long gone now, but I was most intrigued by the mother/son/father relationships, which might well explain your fondness for Shakespeare's *Hamlet*. While you didn't spell it out—perhaps because you were unconscious of it—I saw a profiling of a classic Oedipus complex. Your relationship with your mother, whom you refer to throughout as Von, seems a little, shall we say, intimate. That you characterise her as 'a fusion of Ingrid Bergman, Greta Garbo and Rita Hayworth' is especially interesting, since all these women were temptresses, and none was ever faithful to any one man. Given your parents' separation and divorce, and the sexual abuse inflicted by adults whom you should have been able to trust, your anxiety, resentment and rage—masked by a breezy veneer—is unsurprising. The thrashing delivered by your pater inflicted multiple traumas, of course. No wonder you suffer saudade! What you unconsciously long for *definitely* does *not* exist! You are still aching for the childhood love denied you. No wonder you sought surrogate fathers—magicians, Rosicrucians, fortune-tellers et al—to ameliorate your pain and lead you to the light.

Your call for me to look over your memoir might suggest a search for yet another such guru—hopefully your last—so I'm going to put on my professional therapist hat and suggest that you try to put that beating in an altogether different light. Begin with the thought that your father's own mother had instilled in him (and all her children, I'm sure) an insidious sense of inferiority. Driven by deep anxieties, he went on to 'prove' himself a winner by becoming the star wing of the local rugby team and a successful entrepreneur. But that was not enough. Quite apart from his frustrated desire to be a doctor, he also desperately needed to raise a trophy son. Instead he got a child with a stutter—who became an uncontrollable problem, publicly shaming and humiliating his father, a relatively young man at the time. So the whipping he inflicted was the culmination of a perfect storm. *Three* people got a beating—you, him and his mother. From this distance, we also now see that in the grand Freudian manner you subsequently 'killed' your father, not only by outperforming him, but also, now, by diminishing him at every turn within these pages. That you refer to him as Jack but fail to assign a name to your stepmother is also revelatory of your anger and contempt.

For Freudians like myself, finding a way to kill the father is part of becoming one's own man, and more the norm than the exception. But what about those *two* attempts to end things for yourself? Some might say that your incident inside the Jag was caused by the departure of a lover, Veronica, and the subsequent death of a kindred-spirited, close friend and mentor. I suggest, however, these were mere triggering events, and that the underlying cause was more profound. I want you to consider that both of these near-death experiences happened in your father's proudest possession—his trophy car. You will probably protest that hurtling his Jag into a concrete bridge was an accident. Given the facts and feelings you have set out, however, I see it as a first attempt at suicide. The second go-around is even more telling. I say that because the decision to asphyxiate yourself within the cabin of that very same car was both cool and calculated, more so than even now you seem to realise. What a neat solution your unconscious found for all your issues. It would have ended all your anxieties *and* evened the father/son battle, for he'd never have been able to recover either; he'd be a walking dead man for the rest of his life.

Another way of seeing this is to reflect upon your underlying motivation for breaking into the headmaster's office to steal upcoming exam papers. If you got caught—which I think is what you unconsciously intended—then you would have not only shamed your father, thereby bringing the Big Man down, but you would also have succeeded in punishing yourself and expiating your guilt.

Perhaps most intriguing to me, however, was the way you ultimately evened the score with the Coke character by tupping his wife. I'm guessing that this was just another of your flights of fancy, but no matter. Freudians will say you've described the purest possible case of Oedipal transference; that in your fantasy Coke became your father and you 'killed' him by bedding *your* mother in the form of *his* wife.

You might be aware of all this, but then again perhaps not. Perhaps it was a blind spot that the challenge of writing a memoir retrieved from the depths. You'll be the judge, of course. In any event, you have a wealth of material to work with, so I'm sure you'll have no problem harvesting the 'few inspiring words' you've been asked to share with the latest generation from our old alma mater. I'll be most curious to hear how that all pans out, so be sure to write and let me know.

Yours ever,

Mark

Thanks

Dear Mark,

Thanks! Your insights on the Oedipal thing were especially helpful. Now that I know what was driving me, I might hightail to a confession box and seek forgiveness from the entire cast of characters. (Meantime I'm mulling your cautionary advice to recast everything as a novel.)

The speech is scheduled for tomorrow morning, and it seems that I get to follow my former classmate, Upton Wright, who will impart life lessons from his Rhodes scholarship and his career in pharmaceuticals, where he wound up in the New Jersey headquarters as a vice-president in charge of strategy.

Right now, before I turn in for the night, while all is fresh in my mind, I want to share what happened at this evening's pre-speech dinner in a private room in a Chinatown restaurant. I got there at around six thirty, and save for the headmaster, David Bovey, I was first to arrive.

'Ah, you must be John Wareham,' he said. His handshake was warm and friendly and so was he. Such a handsome young fellow, too, barely forty, and elegantly turned out in blazer, greys, white shirt and a school tie. 'Come on over here,' he said, 'we'll sit together.' Just then everyone started to arrive. Upton—in baggy chinos, white shirt, rep tie and a Brooks Brothers blazer—led in a bunch of younger Old Boys, who, per the fashion these days, were casually dressed and tieless.

Upton and I exchanged pleasantries. He still had a full head of short-back-and-sides hair, though grey. He was trim, though somewhat gaunt, and his bluish complexion hinted of heart pills. Seems his wife, a corporate tax lawyer, gave up her career to raise their boys, one now a doctor, the other a lawyer. We'd have spoken longer, but the masters led in the current high school crop. What a surprise that was! The masters were cheery and turned out in well-pressed greys and blazers, with never a hint of inky tweeds or urine stains. The boys were in their best blazers, too. Nice tailoring, neat barbering, poised demeanours and big, even smiles, no hint of grey, gapped, crooked British teeth. It was impressive. Such was my happy mood, that if a grace was said, it passed me by.

'They tell me you're an aficionado of Shakespeare,' said Bovey.

'I might be the only kid in the country who skipped classes to see *Hamlet*.'

'What'd you think of Olivier's performance?' He knew all about the movie and, apparently, the year it was released. I was surprised.

'A little over the top, but that was the style then. So you're into Shakespeare, too?'

'I love it and I miss it. Before they made me headmaster I taught English. *King Lear* was a favourite.'

His lauding of Lear sounded too good to be true.

'Do you have any favourite lines from *Lear*?'

'Ab-so-lute-ly! Was there ever a more contemptuous line in all of Shakespeare than that which Regan delivers after she has Cornwall pluck out Gloucester's second eye? "Thrust him out of the gate," she says. "He can smell his way to Dover."'

He delivered the words with gusto and aplomb. I became entranced. We talked our way through most of the dinner.

'If only you'd been my English master,' I said.

'Who did you have?'

'Soapy, first.'

'Oh, yes, Soapy.' His shrug and the side-to-side nod of his head spoke volumes. He smiled. 'Do you remember anyone else with special fondness?'

'Coke caught my attention.'

'Ah yes, Coke. Revered by many, but reviled by many also. Just the same, a thousand people attended his funeral. And the gym was named after him.'

'Very, uh, appropriate.'

'So it would seem. You had Wilson, too, right? He taught you Latin.'

'I wish. I was in his class but learned nothing. I might have been to blame, but that's a long story. Whatever went down, I came last and got kicked out.'

'Wilson was ambitious. Seems he wanted to be a famous international novelist, not just a schoolteacher. His writing career began brightly, then faded. History has yet to weigh in. Some say he's oblivion-bound.'

'Oblivion—Fame's eternal dumping ground.'

He grinned, 'Cold storage for high hopes—'

'—a dormitory without an alarm clock.'

We both laughed.

'I guess you know all about him suing the reviewer of his *Sweet White Wine.*'

'Yes. I bet the publishers loved the exposure.'

'And Wilson picked up a year's salary, so maybe all's well that ends well.'

It was, as you've doubtless gathered, a lovely evening, so, on the happiest of notes, I took my leave, stepped out into Chinatown, and headed back to this little hotel room.

Thanks again for your kind insights.

John

P.S. The big day has come and gone! I guess they were keeping costs down because it all happened in a windowless West Side YMCA lecture room so utilitarian that it could have been plucked from the old school building itself. The atmospherics were great, though. Everyone—boys and masters, including the head—was excited. Upton took charge, and after making a copious welcome he launched into a painstakingly prepared speech. 'You're lucky fellows, indeed,' he said to the boys. 'Lucky because you're New Zealanders and doubly lucky because you attend Palmerston North Boys High School, a proven launching-pad for greatness.' As he proceeded to detail his career as a business leader and strategist, I noted a stoop in his shoulders. I guess the boys were suffering jetlag, because many of them seemed a little drowsy. Happily, the phrase 'Let me now finally say' perked them up, and he soon moved to his peroration. 'The *most* important lesson I *ever* learned during my forty-year career comes down to *four* things.' He raised his left hand and proceeded to count. 'First, *identify* a market. Second, *create* a product to fit it. Third, *introduce* it to the market at the lowest price. Then, fourth, *raise* the price.'

We broke for a comfort break and I grabbed a coffee and congratulated Upton for distilling the complexities of a lifetime into such a memorable mantra. After sharing pleasantries we got back to the business of enlightening and inspiring the happy band of up-and-comers.

Now it was my turn. Upton introduced me, noting that he and I had shared the same school years and classes, and noting that I was 'different' from the other fellows. He was about to expand on that, but on a head-shake from me, chose otherwise.

An audience always looks different when you're the speaker. Those faces were so young. They had so much to learn, yet seemed so wise. I felt a surge of something. A jolt from Doctor Moon's million-volt machine? Maybe so. Who was I speaking to? Who indeed? My former self, perhaps. No need to bore you with what I had to say, you know my story, of course.

Best wishes, and again, thanks.

John

A few inspiring words

EDITOR'S NOTE: The following is a transcription of John Wareham's talk to Palmerston North Boys High School students at a gathering in New York.

Okay you guys, you heard it right. I *am* different. I'm different in the same way that each of you is different. We're all unique. We're all special. We're all trying to make sense of life. Are we physical beings on spiritual journeys, or spiritual beings on physical journeys? Do we care? All we need to know for now is that the universe has landed us all in the same place. Whether we're in this world or the next I don't know. I say that because I may be dead already. Let me explain.

If I expired it happened when I was just seventeen. I was waiting for Godot in my father's car. I'd hooked a hose to the tailpipe and fed it into the cabin. Then I hit the ignition. The engine purred and that sickly sweet scent of carbon monoxide invaded my nostrils. I can't be certain of what happened next, so perhaps I'm enjoying the afterlife.

What I seem to recall, however, is that the car stalled, thereby halting one journey and hurling me into another.

It was the stutter I was born with that prompted me to seek a happier place. As I grew older it got worse. Teenage years were torture. By the time I'd finished asking a girl out on a date she'd gone elsewhere.

I seriously contemplated pretending to be mute and restricting all communication to a notepad.

Fortunately, when the car stalled—or seemed to—I saw my impediment in a new light. I must fix it or amount to nothing. Not in this world, anyway.

I withdrew literally every book on stuttering from the local library. Nobody had a cure. Some said speak deliberately and slowly. Some said buy yourself a metronome or beat time with your foot. Some said take up an outdoor sport. Most said stuttering was a psychological problem, a childish way of getting attention. Some said analyse your dreams. Some said just accept it. But nobody knew anything. Indeed, Sigmund Freud remarked, 'The only thing I know about this problem is that it does not respond to psychotherapy.'

But I learned something from a therapist I saw for a couple of months. When psychoanalysis failed, she asked me to read brief passages aloud. I got nowhere and wound up weeping. So then she asked me to 'shadow' her words with my own. 'I will read,' she said, 'and you will listen very closely. The moment I speak a word, say it out loud with me—even as you are listening for the next word. We will go on like this for as long as we can.' As she began, I listened closely. Then—one word at a time, one clause at a time, one sentence at a time—I followed immediately behind her, fluently and effortlessly right to the end. I was astonished. For the first time in my life, I was reading out loud, perfectly, in the presence of another person. So! My stutter was surmountable.

I decided to read aloud for an hour a day. But in the absence of someone for me to 'shadow' I made no progress. So I took to reciting the 107 verses of *The Rubaiyat* of Omar Khayyam. Like shadow reading, the need to focus upon rhythm distracted me from the act of speaking. If I stayed staccato I was okay. But my everyday speech remained in stutter mode. And fitting Khayyam's wisdom into everyday conversations proved difficult (and made me seem daft) so I quit my morning exercises and signed up for a ten-session course in public speaking.

I joined an earnest dozen erstwhile public speakers. Our tutor asked each of us to step to the platform, give our names and read fifty words from a newspaper. My knees shook. My throat went dry. And I mouthed words that refused to exit my lips. The audience was embarrassed and my tutor chagrined.

I attended every session but showed scant improvement. I could merely stumble through a few painful platform minutes, glad not to be among the audience trying to listen.

On the final evening our tutor told of how he'd won the local university's medal for oratory, a coveted prize that attracted aspiring attorneys and politicians.

My tutor was a mousy fellow. If he could win it, so could I. Sure, I still couldn't give a coherent speech. And yes, students winced whenever I appeared. But I vowed, nonetheless, to win that glittering medal.

Failing to apprehend the extent of my impediment, a well-meaning acquaintance recruited me into a swanky public speaking club. The members—mostly barristers, politicians and business leaders—all seemed eight feet tall and all delivered confident, eloquent speeches. I was mesmerised.

At the end of that first evening the chairman sought extemporaneous speakers from the floor. Taking on a life of its own, my arm raised itself and attracted the chairman's eye. My legs walked me up onto the stage. My attempt to talk for my allotted sixty seconds was terrible. When my time was up, the audience applauded politely and the chairman made a kind comment. I returned to my seat, where a couple of other erstwhile speakers—who also happened to be office colleagues—said I'd made a fool of myself. Thank goodness they hadn't been so stupid as to step onto that stage, they said.

Because I kept on going back to the meetings, I was put into a B-grade debating team (there were only two grades) with two young barristers. They were fine, but my tongue-tied efforts wrought our defeat throughout the entire season.

But I was improving. I could make myself understood in everyday life. And onstage I could sometimes string a few flawless sentences together before stumbling.

As the club year drew to a close, the president announced an important national oratory competition. It would be held in a month and was open to all comers.

Oh happy day! This was something I could surely win. Why did I think that I could string a speech together for twelve minutes—or even fit a twelve-minute speech into twelve minutes? Good question. I just had a strange belief in my ability to get everything together for a big occasion.

I worked on a speech to persuade my audience that Neville Chamberlain was one of the greatest British prime ministers who ever lived. The problem was to get the audience to remain open-minded. So I decided to lull the audience into thinking that I was talking about Winston Churchill. I would achieve this by quoting Chamberlain, but making him sound like Churchill. Then, when I revealed that my subject was his polar opposite, the apparently wimpy Neville Chamberlain, the audience would be compelled to listen to make sense of their own misjudgement.

In fact, Churchill had been a lifelong stammerer. He overcame his problem by crafting speeches that read like poetry—then reciting them as if they were poetry. I wanted ultimately to speak like a normal person, so if I opened my talk sounding like Churchill, I might both misdirect the audience and get off to a flying start.

I polished that speech, rehearsed it into a tape recorder and recited it in the shower. Gradually, breath by breath, word by word, sentence by sentence, I crafted what I hoped was a seamless speech running almost like blank verse.

In the week prior to competition, I spoke in a debate—and again came last. Some friends suggested that in fairness to myself and my club I should quit.

Then I met a sage. Ben O'Connor had won every important national speaking competition. He agreed to have me rehearse before him in his office. He said little except that I should take more time over my pauses, clearly enunciate word endings and speak from the heart. My stutter became less and less of a problem. Finally, Ben turned to me, 'This is the twenty-fifth year of the contest, so it will be a big turnout and the competition will be tough. But I believe you can win.'

The competition, before a sell-out black-tie audience in an intimate theatre, honoured an airman who'd died in the Battle of Britain. I arrived in a rented tuxedo and spotted the snickering colleagues who'd given me such frank advice on my first club evening.

I'd drawn final place on the programme, so I would hear all the speeches before delivering my own. A spotlit, solemn, black-ribboned photo of the handsome young pilot whose name the competition honoured stood on a desk on the stage. I glanced at my cue cards, then tossed them aside. I studied the young airman's photo and imagined myself giving a speech to make his family proud.

I grew more confident as each speaker came and went. They weren't as well prepared as I. They seemed pressured by the occasion. They were talented and competent, but no longer eight feet tall.

Now the favoured winner and second-to-last speaker rose to the stage. Tall, imposing, radiating self-confidence, he spoke in a rich, resonant voice. His polished, professional performance impressed the audience and won the best applause of the evening. He sat down confidently. He'd heard me speak on other occasions. He knew that only a miracle could save me.

Now it was my turn. I climbed the stage and gazed over the sea of faces till they settled. I stood stock still, took a deep breath, then evenly and effortlessly began . . .

The next twelve minutes seemed magical. The audience responded to my own excitement. They seemed to draw my speech from me. I seemed to become a mere vehicle for greater thoughts and feelings. My opening quote piqued attention. Then I revealed that my subject was not Churchill but Chamberlain and the astonished audience leaned forward and hung on every word. I finally exited the stage to momentary stunned silence. Then the applause began and swelled and continued.

The adjudicator knew nothing of my history. He critiqued each speaker in turn, then he turned to me. He paid me many compliments, then wound up with these words, 'I have placed Mister Wareham best speaker by such a wide margin that I decline to place anyone else. He is clearly a natural orator with a God-given voice.'

I remembered the story of the clergyman, who, passing by the beautiful home of one of his brethren, commented, 'God has given you a wonderful garden.'

'Yes,' came the reply, 'but you should have seen it when God had it on his own!'

If I really am dead already, it'll be okay to confess some things I've learned on this side of the curtain.

As far as I can tell, the way to create a heaven is to select words wisely and send them out softly. The movers and shakers among the angels—and some of the devils, too, alas—are doing just that.

The apprehension of failure is inevitably worse than failure itself. The cure is to plunge ahead. Be bold and all sorts of saints and sages—disguised as regular people—will pop up to help.

Where you stumble, there lies your treasure. To control my breathing I learned to pause—and often drop my voice—where other speakers simply sped on by. As I fell silent, the audience hushed and leaned forward in their chairs, as if hypnotised. At that point, I could choose, if I wished, to shift the pace and pitch. This ingrained tendency to hesitate, this confusing, underlying vulnerability, this blend of light and shade, this curious rhythmic pattern, turned out to be a priceless gift.

As you know, your high school has the same name as mine. It is also in the same town and in the same place on the same street. But no one steps into the same river twice. Youth is difficult and life can be, too. It was for me, and I'm betting it is for you, too. But embrace your travails now, and they'll turn to treasure later. As to getting along with others, I like the advice of Philo of Alexandria, 'Be kind, for everyone you meet is fighting a great battle.' You're all fighting great battles, too,

I'll bet. To help you win, I'd like to leave you with a favourite poem by my good friend Chandler Haste:

> *In the dream, your heart sought the sky before*
> *you did, and started to soar of its own*
> *free will; free in the moment it foreswore*
> *the throng to fly to a fortune unknown.*
> *Inspired by that courage you followed suit,*
> *flouting the doubts of inhibiting friends,*
> *gliding past cynics in unbound pursuit*
> *of the helix your heart said ascends*
> *to the life you've been chosen to live,*
> *if only you'll kindly yield to embrace*
> *the earnest pleas of that soul-starved plaintiff*
> *whose appeals you'd persistently debased*
> *—until your aching heart fled for the clouds*
> *resolved to save the only life it could.*

The weird thing that happened

Dear Mark:

Here I am again. Why so quickly? Well, because I absolutely must share the weird thing that happened after I thought I'd finished with the delivery of my 'few inspiring words'.

I was, as you might imagine, both elated and exhausted. In that mood, I figured I might treat myself to a fifty-minute massage before heading home. I had entered a nearby Asian parlour and was about to disrobe, when a silky voice caught my attention.

'Hey, Johnny!'

I parted the curtain and peered out the window. Was that really him, in the shadow of that doorway? I ran outside and crossed the street. 'Is that you, Doc?'

'You're all grown up now, Johnny, so drop the Doc thing. Call me Irwin.'

'You truly are Doctor Irwin A. Moon?'

'Of course,' he grinned, 'didn't jolt you, did I?'

I ignored the pun and grabbed his hand. 'Wow! You look exactly the same as fifty years ago. How can that be? And whatever in the world are you doing here?'

'Come on inside, Johnny, I'll show you.' He pressed the door open and I followed him. 'It's my latest laboratory, see.'

'Very impressive.'

'I've been doing some interesting things—astonishing to most people, but common sense to you and me. Here, come into the boardroom.' He stepped to a black door, pushed it open and waved me inside. The walls were white, the carpet charcoal and the furnishings sparse. Two red chairs sat at opposite ends of an oval onyx table, in the middle of which sat a glowing red button. 'Take a seat, Johnny.'

'What sorts of things are you doing?'

'I'm working on resurrections.'

'You're bringing back the dead?'

'Not quite. Right now I'm merely manifesting visible spirits that we can see and talk to.'

'Why do you think I might not be amazed?'

'Because you've had time to mull my earlier demonstration.'

'The million-volt thing? Well, yes, I thought it over and read up on quantum science. I'm well and truly into the idea of two worlds.'

'Physical and spiritual?'

'Something like that. Spiritual mightn't be the right word. And I have to confess that your attempt to link electrical currents to the Genesis and the Resurrection still leaves me cold.'

'I've moved on, too, Johnny.'

'Of course, I mean, you're dead, right?'

'I'm Schrödinger's Cat—dead in one world and alive in another,' he grinned, 'like Christ in his tomb.'

'Let's not rehash that,' I joshed. 'Just tell me whose world we're in now?'

'You stepped across the barrier, Johnny. You're in my world. And you're here for a reason. You've unfinished business to attend to.'

'My karma is calling?'

'Maybe the karma's not your own. Maybe you need to attend to someone else's.'

'Like whose?'

'Is there anyone you'd like to catch up with?'

'You can resurrect someone right here and now?'

'Someone dead is dying to meet you, Johnny.' He grinned. 'That's why you're here. You believe in synchronicity, right?'

'Karma, synchronicity, entangled atoms, I can believe in anything and everything. Could you possibly conjure up Soapy or Wilson or Coke?'

'Sure! We'll pow-wow with them right away.' He reached over and set his hand above the glowing red button. 'Watch *this*!' He hit the button and three circles opened in the floor, each belching fire. Then three red chairs ascended. Could it be? Yes. Soapy, Wilson and Coke, all sweating profusely, all staring vacantly, were seated on those stools. The circles closed and the flames disappeared, leaving a strange otherworldly scent.

'They don't get out from the underworld very often, so they're a little dazed,' said Irwin. 'I should add that we only have a few minutes before the batteries run out, so kick the session into gear, Johnny. Ask them a question.'

They looked much the same as I remembered, but on closer inspection were naked save for inky academic gowns.

'Will they remember me?'

'You've changed a lot, and not just physically, Johnny, so it might be difficult for you to tap down into their mostly stagnant wavelength. It's a funny thing about hell. It sizzles the flesh but unless there's been intellectual and emotional progress it freezes both brain and heart. But try them with a query. They can't see or hear me, but they will see and hear you.'

'Hi guys.' Nobody smiled. 'Is it true that the three of you worked on the novel that caused all the fuss?' Their eyes widened.

'*Sweet White Wine* was a truly great novel,' said Wilson. 'The prophecy that it would secure my place in history has come true. My books are in print in every language. I am famous throughout the world.'

'Oh poor Guthrie,' said Irwin. 'He truly believes all that. He's making no progress. He'll never get out.'

'I worked on the grammar only,' said Soapy. 'I made every sentence perfect.'

'Perfect?' Irwin raised his eyebrows. 'Poor devil! The book is dull and pretentious. After all these years, this soapy English master remains a tone-deaf technocrat. It'll be a cold day in hell before they ever turn him loose.'

Coke stirred, clenched his fists, stretched his arms wide and blinked. 'What's a novel?' he asked.

'Ah, an admission of ignorance!' Irwin was elated. 'Such a confession might just signal incipient humility. There may be hope for this fellow, Johnny.' He paused. 'Is there anyone else you'd like to see?'

'Can we locate Potts?'

'That might be even easier, actually.'

He touched the button and the ceiling opened. Potts, clad in glistening robes, descended on a golden trapeze. His silver sandals hovered above the table. 'Johnny! Johnny! Johnny!' he exclaimed, warmly. 'Oh how I've been praying we might meet again.'

You looked up into his gleaming glasses. 'Really?'

'Yes, really. I've repented, of course. That was enough for God, but not for me. I've always yearned to catch up with you and make man-to-man amends.'

'Man-to-man?'

'Oh, Johnny! You always had an ear for the double entendre. But you know what I mean, right?'

'You're not miffed that I turned you in?'

'No, Johnny, no! You did the right thing. I was ashamed, of course. Who wouldn't be? But I was never angry with you.'

'You felt shame?'

He scratched his head, then grinned. 'If I'm less than honest— and I mean less than *totally* honest—they'll kick me downstairs,' he said. 'So let me clarify. Yes, I felt shame. I was ashamed of being gay and of getting found out. But that was then and this is now. Nowadays I'm proud to be gay, because, well, that's the way that God made me. My yearning to make amends with you is because I know that I was a malignant force. I'd never have *turned* you gay, of course. No one can do that. My crime was to create a clandestine, isolating, alienating web, within an already problematic setting, then try to quell my loneliness by betraying all trust, wantonly drawing children like yourself into it and corrupting their innocence.'

'Understanding trumps remorse, Johnny—he's out of hell forever now.' Irwin glanced at his watch. 'Alas, we've only time for one last question.'

I knew exactly what to ask.

'Is the infliction of pain an important element of a high-school education?'

Wilson and Soapy exchanged glances.

'Spare the rod and spoil the child,' said Soapy.

'Yes indeed—I second that,' said Wilson.

'There's enough pain in the world to stoke the fires of hell for all eternity,' said Potts. 'What we need to pass along is kindness.'

'What's an infliction?' said Coke.

'Time's running out, Johnny. Don't miss the biggest opportunity of your life.'

'What've I gotta do, Doc?'

The circles reopened.

'The karmic moment is at hand, Johnny. You must speak up. They'll all be gone in a moment, as will you.' Potts was indeed rising heavenward. The flames were hissing and the chairs were descending into the fire. 'Say the words, Johnny! Say them, for Christ's sake! Say them *now!*'

In that moment, I awoke to find myself inside the incense-laden parlour, face upward on a massage table, surrounded by steaming stones, naked save for a towel, clutching the masseur and screaming at the ceiling chandelier, 'I forgive you, I forgive you, I forgive you!' ●

Epilogue

Eyes and fingers

I originally considered turning this memoir into a work of fiction. But that seemed a dodge. So I called upon my childhood self to share what he experienced.

Soon enough, reader responses taught me that his feelings were universal and that people all over the world behave much the same. Well, yes of course. We all have to create ourselves, and most of us encounter similar sets of human archetypes along the way.

But, this being a memoir, and since my early self was purporting to be a photographer, the same readers asked me why I didn't include photos of the denizens I'd written about.

The answer—that I deliberately omitted photos hoping that words alone might create a more vivid picture—didn't satisfy. So, I decided take another look at my files.

I found that the boy I used to be had indeed created enough images for me to apply some healing salt and sunlight to some festering wounds. He'd also kept a set of high school yearbooks, *Pamerstonians,* with some of his shots in the mix.

Finally, after some reflection, I decided, hopefully for the greater good, to bow to my readers and add a few images and names.

Some characters looking up from the afterlife may be chagrined that I blended boyhood eyes with adult fingers to record iniquities not uncommon to the era.

Yes, of course; that was then and this is now.

I'm sure we all matured and repented any miscreant behaviors.

I know I did, mostly.

**Psychologists tell
us that the key** to
understanding oneself
is to take a close look
your father's mother. So
I did. Here, left, is a shot
of Eve as a young lady.

And here, above, I captured her,
now an aging matriarch, leaning
back upon Jack's Mark VII Jag.

These, left, were her three sons.
From front to back, Pat, Jack,
and Morris.

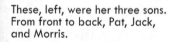

Perhaps this party shot of
Jack and Eve, below, reveals
something of the influence she
wielded.

I took this kitchen shot of Jack, left, in 1953.

And this one, below, 20 years later, in his garage.

And, here, he is, right, in his twenties.

EPILOGUE

Old family photos can reveal a lot about social expectations. Left to right, here are my mother Von, her brother Cecil, and her sister Gwen.

Things don't always play out as planned, but Von always had smile, and, rain or shine, she was always fun to be with.

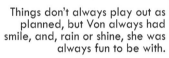

Brian Sutton-Smith, our esteemed teacher, was decidedly there for me, but, alas, is absent from this photo of the Newtown, Wellington public school class that took me following my failure to respond appropriately to Marist Brothers teachings. I'm second from the left in the third row.

Brian moved on to become
Dr. Brian Sutton-Smith, iconic
professor of psychology at
Columbia University. Here,
left, his laser smile and natural
empathy are on display.
You might like this one of
his best known quotes: 'The
opposite of play isn't work. It is
depression.'

By sheer chance, or synchronicity, perhaps, I met up with Brian in
New York, and we became close friends. He was lost in thought and
looking every inch the visionary sage when I snapped the above
shot of him during a quiet lunch we shared at the University Club.

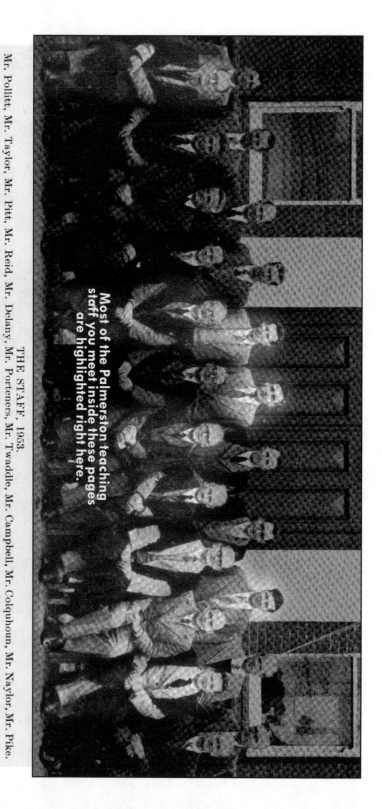

Most of the Palmerston teaching staff you meet inside these pages are highlighted right here.

THE STAFF, 1953.

Mr. Pollitt, Mr. Taylor, Mr. Pitt, Mr. Reid, Mr. Delany, Mr. Porteners, Mr. Twaddle, Mr. Campbell, Mr. Colquhoun, Mr. Naylor, Mr. Pike. Mr. Stowe, Mr. Gore, Mr. Skoglund, Mr. McKay, Mr. Smith, Mr. Kerr, Mr. Begg, Mr. Doel, Mr. McDonald, Mr. Salter, Mr. Wilson,Mr. Hobin

O.J. Begg, Headmaster from 1947 to 1954. The boys called him Peggy.

'Soapy' McDonald, head of the welcoming committee and my third form English master.

No nickname seemed necessary for **R.S. Craven,** who took over from Begg in 1954.

'Grubby' Salter. My first math teacher.

I took this shot of my dorm mates on their first night away from home.

Before turning out the lights, that night, housemaster A.K. Stowe, nickname of Potts (left), kindly accepted my camera from my hands and snapped this one of me (right).

Here, left again, I captured Potts satisfying himself that we're comfortable before turning out the lights.

Potts appreciated the value of high jinks and trusted that it inspired equally high morale. So, to your left, favoring a little levity, he applies a firm pair of hands to hoisting the College House Guy Fawkes dummy aloft.

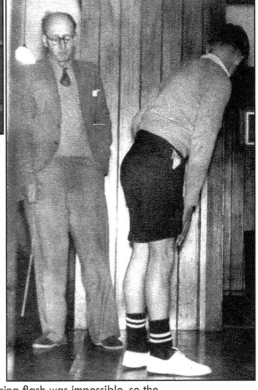

My good friend and mischievous collaborator, Ian Chandler, was due to be disciplined so he agreed to let me sneak this shot of Potts administering four bamboo lashes. To be fair, Potts never drew blood. And, in this case, Ian had surreptitiously loaded a protective layer of thick felt between his butt and his trousers. The light was dim and using flash was impossible, so the quality of the photo is poor. But at least it exists.

Potts waited for me to take this shot, before doling out my weekly newly
minted silver half-crown of pocket money; always a memorable moment.

```
                                              College House 'Phone   5639
                                              School 'Phone  - - -   5156
    College House,
    Boys' High School,
         Palmerston North, ......7...-...5...-........... 1954

M. J. Wareham
   207 Ohiro Rd
     Wellington                              No    660
```

Statement of Expenditure

For *Roger Wareham*   1st Term, 1954

Stationery & Books	*Bennetts*		1	12	5
	Science magazine	2	5	4
Clothes, Repairs, Cleaning			9	1
Pocket Money		1	5	-
Collections, Subscriptions, Stamps			12	-
Travelling Expenses		1	1	9
Sundries	*Badminton club*		12	6
			8	6
			1	-	-
	£	9	13	7
	credit sale book		11	-
	£	9	2	7

Extravagant with books and stationery.

Restored to IV.A. John is doing excellently; becoming steadier in every way — Conduct excellent

Here, in Potts own hand, is a copy of a monthly statement and report supplied to my father to show that his investment in his son's education was in safe and caring hands. The advice that the hitherto mediocre student has been returned to the A-Stream fourth form class, and 'is doing excellently . . . becoming steadier in every way . . . conduct excellent' was doubtless gratifying. And, 'Extravagant with books and stationery' is a subtle compliment, surely.

Guthrie Wilson won promotion for his fighting spirit. Here he is (left) in 1943, part way through WWII.

Here, above, he sits at his typewriter, recounting what went down in battle.

And here, above, a decade later, in full regalia, apparently reliving old dreams and past glories, Gus leads a 'battalion' of furry cheeked Palmerston North high school boys through their compulsory military training.

Here, left, again in battle dress, he poses for a photo with a Palmerston North Boys High School rugby team.

I risked a whipping when I snuck this shot of Gus in his Latin class. Heart in mouth, I upped the ante, and asked him to sign the print I created. Fortunately for me he liked what he saw and signed the photo.

Ian Colquhoun, nickname of Coke, rose from humble origins and overcame the lack of formal academic credentials to become gym teacher and house master. He prided himself on his athleticism and coaching skills.

College House was a breeding ground for top players. Below and highlighted are the boarders who made the 1955 1st XV. In the middle row is my good friend, 'Big Man' Colin McKay; in back, left to right, are Barry Gibson and Graham 'Ginger' Wilson; both worked wonders on the field.

1st XV, 1955.
Back Row.—W. Waka, B. Gibson, J. Robinson, B. Clarke, G. Wilson.
Second Row.—Mr. Colquhoun, J. Millar, C. McKay, L. Wilde, G. Mitchell, K. Eglinton.
Front Row.—R. Pilkinton, R. Eglinton, N. Plimmer, D. Woods (capt.), D. Berriman (vice-capt.). B. Anderson. N. Henson.

Survivors of the 1957 1st XV after the headmaster suspended wayward members. The underwhelming replacement team seemed destined for debacle. And, as you know, the outcome in the only game they ever played together proved a shocker.

THE PREFECTS, 1956.
Back Row: L. Gloyn, R. Eyles, J. Millar, L. Meade, B. Clarke, R. Clifton.
Front Row: J. Toomath, R. Griggs, M. Howell, B. Gibson (head), D. Waite, J. Smith, J. Lucas.

Palmerston North Boys High School trusted the British prefect system to create an elite hierarchy of righteous young fellows, and mostly it did.

Oscar Dole, a decent chap, was always on the scene. I snuck this photo above during a fourth form history class. He became Craven's first assistant.

Oscar might have seemed a little dour but he was always reasonable, always down to earth.

Coke also ran the boxing tournament. A showcase event, it lasted a week, and the black tie finale attracted a big audience. Critics of this 'sport' were answered thus in the yearbook:

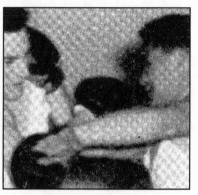

'Boxing is good because the boxers enjoy it – not in the way that you enjoy a milkshake, but in the way you enjoy nervousness, tension, proof of yourself and achievement . . . Those who have not been in the ring reveal a lust for sensation. Boxing is probably bad for *them*. They should not come.'

Some boys relished the chance to show their fighting prowess. Others had to be coaxed into the ring. I shot the photos and signed on for the 'Midget' class, thereby winning a yearbook mention: 'Wareham was game and threw everything he had into a fruitless attack.'

The referee above is noted mathematics master, Dr. W.A.C. Smith, His nickname was Wack, but he was mostly light on the cane. He authored the national mathematics textbook, and was a first class teacher. In the striped jersey you see my dormmate David Henshaw, a fine athlete, but sensitive, too. He became an acclaimed watercolorist.

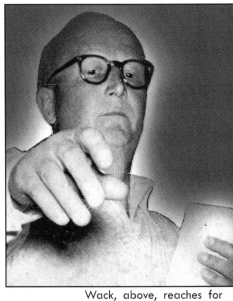

Wack, above, reaches for the decisions of the three dinner-suited judges.

Potts, right, rapt in concentration, ponders the swinging beauties.

Here's the big 1954 school championship finale. Evans (left) and Berriman (right), could both throw killer punches. With raw honesty, the yearbook noted 'Evans stormed in with a vicious two-handed attack which left no doubt about the decision. It was a very good final between two first-class pugilists'.

John Lucas (above) a valued member of the school's semi-secret cult of Christian Crusaders asked me to get this shot of him in full flight. Alas, he choked whenever faced with the lofty lobs and feathery drop shots of my good friend Warren Satherley (above right), whose craft in any sport was devilish. Both made the tennis team, as you see below.

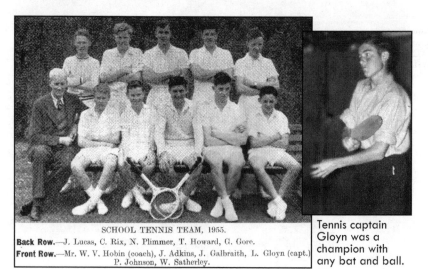

SCHOOL TENNIS TEAM, 1955.

Back Row.—J. Lucas, C. Rix, N. Plimmer, T. Howard, G. Gore.
Front Row.—Mr. W. V. Hobin (coach), J. Adkins, J. Galbraith, L. Gloyn (capt.)
P. Johnson, W. Satherley.

Tennis captain Gloyn was a champion with any bat and ball.

Experimenting with the camera was my obsession. Here, my boarder roommate Ted Swanney holds my day-boy classmate John Reid in the palm of his hand.

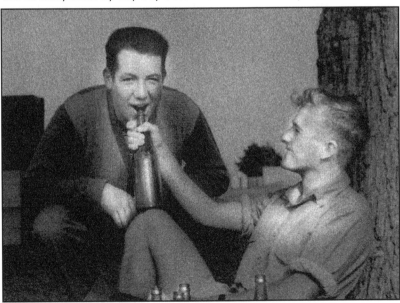

Brewing hops and fermenting grapes were other ways to pass the time. Here, Ted pretends to hold the fluid of such a distillation to the lips of cohort 'Tubby' Taylor, who was more tough than tubby, and always a great guy.

My hidden camera snatched this photo of music master Steve Delaney.
When he abruptly resigned in 1955, I invested my pocket money in a box of
chocolates, sought him out, and presented it. 'I'm sorry if I messed up in your
class,' I said. He eyed me doubtfully, broke open the package, and cast a hard
look at the chocolates, perhaps to see if any had been injected with poison. 'Let
me see you eat one first,' he said, softly. I did just that. 'So then I'll join you.' He
quaffed a caramel, then, pleased and surprised by my gesture, reached out
sand shook my hand. He truly was a nice person.

'The devil himself has sent those firecrackers.' That's what housemaster Gus
Portners was probably thinking. My tennis partner Warrren Satherley and my
mischievous friend Ian Chandler, left to right, inspect the bangers. Peeking in,
sometime boxer and watercolorist David Henshaw.

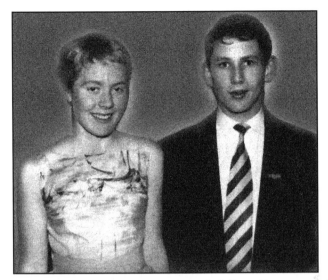

I rigged a rudimentary studio for the inaugural College House end-of-year ball. Like most young ladies who chose to attend, my fairest of the fair partner, Barbara, hailed from Palmerston Girls High School.

I also captured these chaperones. I'm unsure of all the names. Headmaster Craven towers in the back. Coke's wife, foxy furred Betty Colquhoun, is in front of him. In black next to Craven is Matron. Coke and Oscar are far right. Seated in front are housemasters Rose and Rutherford.

My brother Mike

I omitted all reference to my brother from this schooldays memoir. Our relationship seemed irrelevant. Here's why.

Our parents split when I was five, and Mike was nearly four years my junior, so we shared mere months under the same roof. Our so-called family never had a meal together.

Mike and I lived in different houses. He lived with Jack and the Cigarilloed One. I wound up with Von and her low-life lover.

Mike and I were both baptized Roman Catholic. He fell under the spell. I did not. We never attended the same school. Then I got sent to boarding college, and so, for five years, we lived in different cities.

Mike played classical piano and painted watercolors.

I was into the magic arts and shoplifting.

Mike desperately needed the comfort of a big brother.

I never wanted a brother. And I never truly was one.

I was alone and needed to survive. I became self-reliant and resilient, and trusted nobody.

Mike was warm and generous, and always admired his non-brother.

Back in Wellington, a week before this memoir was to be released, I'd still not given Mike a copy. He'd surely be offended not to get a mention. Might he also see my words as jaundiced and disloyal?

One day later, ill at ease, I reluctantly set my creation into his hands.

To my surprise he was elated. His brother was presenting him with a gift. He smiled warmly. "Great cover," he said. "I'm going to rush off home and read it tonight. And I'll give you my report on it tomorrow. Promise."

Next afternoon, we sat on my apartment deck.

"Wow! It was an eye-opener, John." He beamed a smile and grabbed my hand. "Congratulations!" His grip was warm. "I just *love* absolutely *everything* you've written." He shone a knowing smile. "And it was really smart to keep me out of it."

A couple of years later, Mike died.

I could write a book about how those last days played out.

No joint family photo exists. Von booked the studio for the one on the left.

Mike showed up briefly at Von's house. I set up the photo and she took it. Mike and I are sitting atop the homemade trolley I'd crafted from some of stolen planks and steel ball bearing roller wheels. I liked to careen downhill on it, scaring otherwise upwardly mobile old ladies.

I took this shot of us on a Tuesday in Mike's garden. We set a lunch date for Friday. Alas, that was not to be. The fellow with the sickle got there first.

I shot this of Jack on his 90th Birthday.

And Von on hers, too (and, as I recall, the hand held portrait of 60 years earlier).

A few years after Jack and Von relocated
to the Other Place, I snapped this shot of
Mike celebrating the birthday of one of his
granddaughters.

Self Portrait, age nine, toasting myself on an autumn day in a Wellington park on the warm steel of First World War artillery.

Intrigued by the sight of a 12-year-old prowling around town with a Leica, Wellington photographer Robert H. Smith invited me into his studio and snapped this shot. I returned the favor with this inset one of him.

John Wareham is confidant, coach, and counsellor to corporate leaders at one end of the social spectrum, and prison residents and those returning on the other. He is also a widely published writer of non-fiction, fiction, and poetry. His work includes the business best-sellers *Secrets of a Corporate Headhunter* and *The Anatomy of a Great Executive*; the crossover life-changers *How to Break Out of Prison* and *How to Survive a Bullet to the Heart*; the acclaimed novels *Chancey On Top* and *The President's Therapist (and the Secret Intervention to Treat the Alcoholism of George W. Bush)*, which introduced John's alter-ego in the form of fictional psychoanalyst Dr. Mark Alter; and the poetry anthology *Sonnets for Sinners*. John has led seminars and symposia in most world cities, is an in-demand keynote speaker, and a member of the international writers group PEN. He resides mostly in New York and Wellington, New Zealand. A sometime yachtsman, he skippered his yacht to win division and class in the Sydney to Hobart ocean race. His spare-time interests include photography, movies, theater, opera, and golf.

Talking Your Way *to the* TOP

The Nervous Person's Heaven Sent
Overnight Guide to Public Speaking

JOHN WAREHAM

Illustrated by Anthony Viola

'John Wareham's cool, clear wisdom' and
'Nietzschean strategies' inspire the otherwise
'inexplicable desire to listen.'
New York Times

The Secrets of Potent Public Presentation

How to turn nervous energy to charismatic gold and deliver the presentation of your life.

*'John Wareham's cool, clear wisdom' and 'Nietzschean strategies'
inspire the otherwise 'inexplicable desire to listen.'*
—New York Times.
*'John's magic transforms ordinary citizens into inspiring orators—
I've seen him do it.'*
—Mitch Rosenthal, M.D., CEO, Phoenix House
*'A secret weapon... tells how to deliver a message that commands
respect in any company.'*
—Lt. General, Jack Klimp U.S. Marine Corps (rtd)

Available from Flatiron Press, or online at Amazon

Made in United States
Orlando, FL
08 November 2023

38732527R00161